THE BRITISH JOURNAL OF PHOTOGRAPHY ANNUAL

1972

The British Journal of Photography Annual is the oldest publication of its kind in the world. It first appeared in the form of a wall calendar for the year 1860 and was issued as a supplement to 'The British Journal of Photography' of December 15, 1859. A facsimile was published in the 1969 edition.

For the first five years after its inception, 1861–65, The British Journal Photographic Almanac, as it was then known, was 4 x $2\frac{1}{2}$ inches in size and it was issued free of charge to subscribers to the Journal.

The 1886 issue was produced with a crown 8vo format and was sold as a separate publication. This format remained unchanged for 97 years until the 1964 issue, when the present format was adopted.

Successive Editors of the Annual:

1861–62	Samuel Highley
1863	James Martin
1864	Emerson J. Reynolds
1865–79	J. Traill Taylor
1880–86	W. B. Bolton
1887–96	J. Traill Taylor
1897–1905	Thomas Bedding
1906–1934	George E. Brown
1935	{ H. W. Bennett / P. C. Smethurst
1936	{ H. W. Bennett / Arthur J. Dalladay
1937–67	Arthur J. Dalladay
1968–	Geoffrey Crawley

Picture Editors:

1964	Bryn Campbell
1965–1967	Norman Hall
1968	Ainslie Ellis
1969	{ Anna Körner / Geoffrey Crawley
1970–71	Anna Körner
1972	Mark Butler

THE BRITISH JOURNAL
OF PHOTOGRAPHY
ANNUAL 1972

Editor
GEOFFREY CRAWLEY

Picture Editor
MARK BUTLER

Published by
Henry Greenwood & Co. Ltd.,
24 Wellington Street,
London, WC2

Library of Congress Catalog Card Number 65-80513
ISBN 900414 03 0

Printed in Great Britain by
The Lewes Press Ltd. Friars Walk, Lewes, Sussex

Foreword

With its 113th edition, *The British Journal of Photography Annual* again places before its readers the blend of pictures, feature articles and technical information which in recent years has gained for it a larger international following. It is interesting now to look back over the eight editions which have appeared in the enlarged format. The photograph more than the painting seems tied in style to its own era and this is nowhere apparent than when studying the photographs reproduced in the old-style annuals of years ago.

When one is close to the photography of a particular year in the Annual, it is rather difficult to characterise it in the way that it will be seen in its context historically. Today, the photographer is primarily interested in the world around him, at least this would seem to be the main pre-occupation judging from the work we are shown. The present generation has learned to feel visually, to an extent and in a manner which earlier generations did not. The increasing speed of modern life, particularly in the cities, has given less time for the absorption of information and interest through the spoken and the printed word. Today the emphasis is what the sociologists term visual-tactile—in other words we see and we touch and information comes to our senses more through these channels than hitherto. They are the senses through which information can more rapidly be assimilated even if, alas, this very fact makes a visual-tactile generation less stable and more prone to a trial and error approach in their lives and their interests. The photographer of today is desperately anxious to use his camera to bring home to people—the complacent and the smug—the fact that beyond their own front gardens the world may be a very different place. He brings to photography, however, one quality which serves a most vital function in a society which appears to become increasingly involved in economic and materialistic rat races. This is his insistence that photography should not record coldly but with humanity. Today, we hear much spoken of the alternative society and if this alternative society has come into being, it is only because the rest of us have been deceived by our own propaganda and come to believe that materialistic, commercial, technologically progressive and economic aims express the true purpose of society. On the contrary, the origins of organised society were to foster and protect the individual, so that by pooling skills' of the hand with some and of the brain with others' an effective and protective unit could be established in which the human values could find expression. As this fundamental aim becomes obscured, as the vortices of commercialism suck more and more of the humanity of mankind into their cold objectives, it is natural that the artist—and here we include the photographer—should be the one who stands out and protests. Since he is protesting, it follows that he should tend to emphasise poverty, sickness and despair although he is as aware as anyone that such subjects are not representative of the whole of the world around him. In this year's Annual we have tried to show a fair spectrum of the work of the artist-photographers of today.

For many readers the technical section of the Annual has been, over the years, a prime motive for collecting each subsequent edition and in this, the 1972 Annual, he will find that the sections dealing with colour and black-and-white processing have been fully revised and updated. Attention is also drawn to the updating provided for us by Ilford Limited, which is applicable to the toning of modern bromide papers; to some extent the term 'bromide' is a misnomer today, since the majority are virtually chloro-bromide types. The Epitome of Progress section this year is particularly full with an excellent review of materials for colour photography and a new addition deals with education in photography, a subject with which the columns of the 'BJ' are increasingly concerned. It is worth putting on record as we write, for readers in the future, that the photographic trade in Great Britain has been going through a very bad period which now seems to be moving into a more hopeful time. Currently the subject of Britain's entry into the EEC is being hotly debated and its effect on photography and the photography trade seems still very much an unknown factor. Photography is, however, as these pages show, an international language and it is difficult to believe other than that a greater unity with Europe would prove advantageous.

Today *The British Journal of Photography Annual* is reaching an increasingly large number of overseas readers and to these, as well as those at home, we wish every success in the coming year and lay this 1972 edition of the world's founder yearbook before them with the hope that they will find it once again entertaining, informative, and perhaps here and there thought-provoking.

GEOFFREY CRAWLEY, FRPS, DGPh
Editor

September, 1971

Contents

Picture Section—9-135

Blocks by Commercial Process Limited

SONYA HIRSCH

BELOW AND OPPOSITE
ROD WILLIAMS

DAVID NEWELL SMITH   SONYA HIRSCH

BERRIS
CONNOLLY

JOHN
RUDD

JAMES FEE

PAUL CARTER

DAVID NEWELL SMITH

JOHN STONEX

L. BORODULIN

26

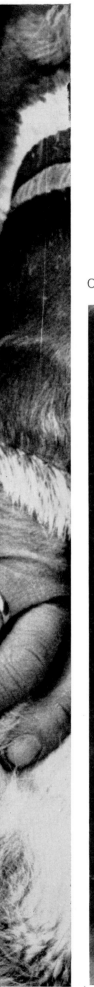

O. TSESARSKY

BILL CARTER

IAN STER

RAGHU RAI

. TSESARSKY

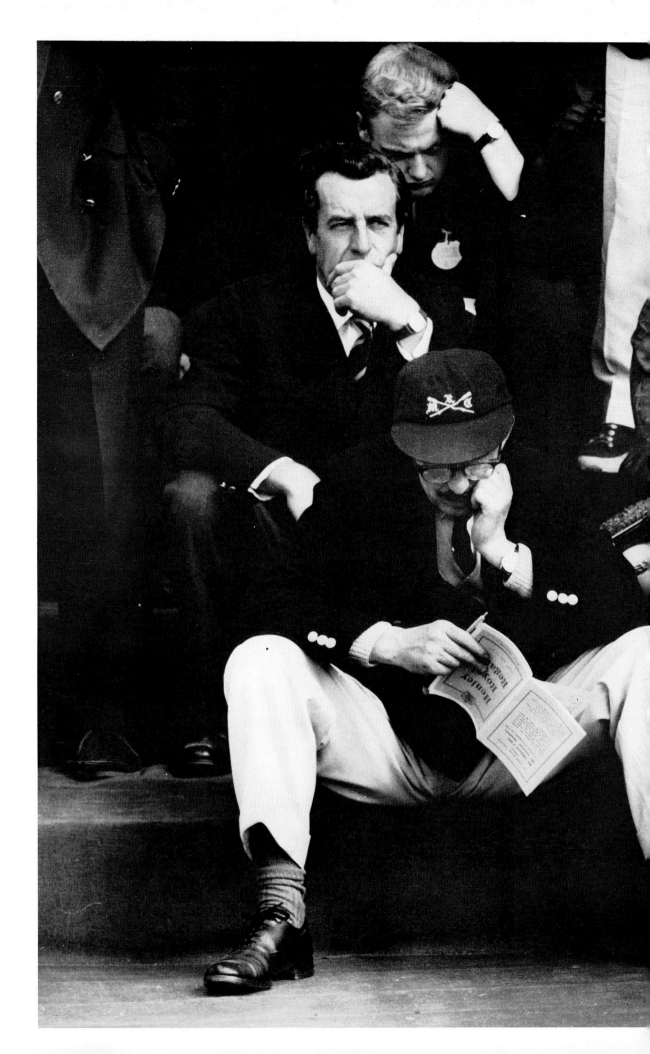

JOHN
COWAN

NORMAN WIGGINS

SRDJA DJUKANOVIC

KURT AIGNER

DAVID NEWELL SMITH

HOMER SYKES

Melchior Digiacomo

Melchior Digiacomo who recently visited this country on an assignment to photograph rugby-football, started work some 10 years ago as an usher in the New York television studio of CBS. He worked his way up to the post of advertising manager for on-air promotions and it was his friendship with a TV producer that initiated his interest in photography. The producer was actually working on outside broadcasts of football games and photographed them with his still camera at the same time. Digiacomo's work appears regularly in USA periodicals and the photographs here are from a series showing 'the other side of the coin' in New York.

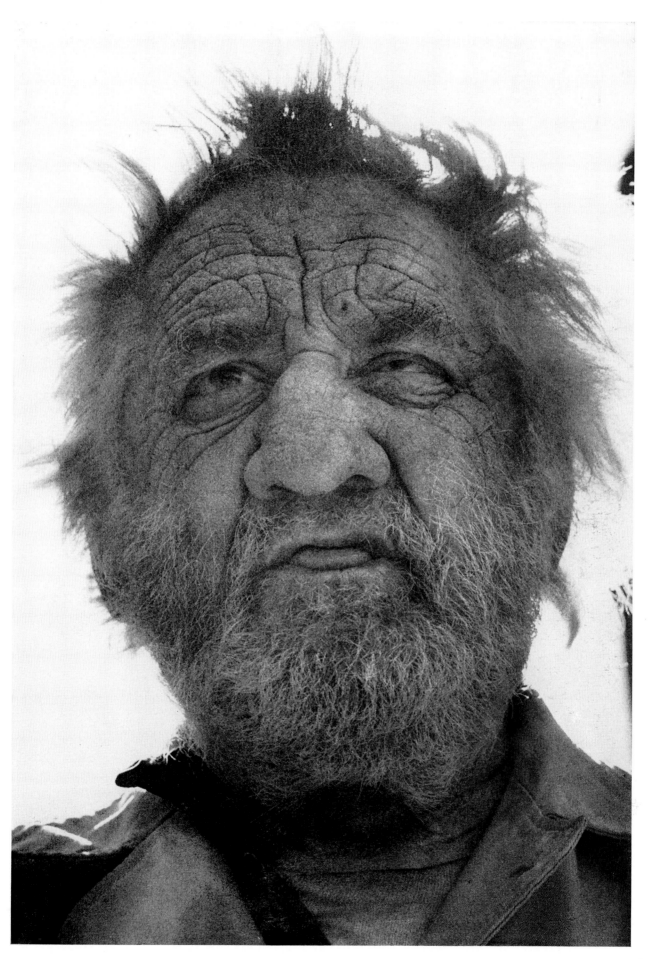

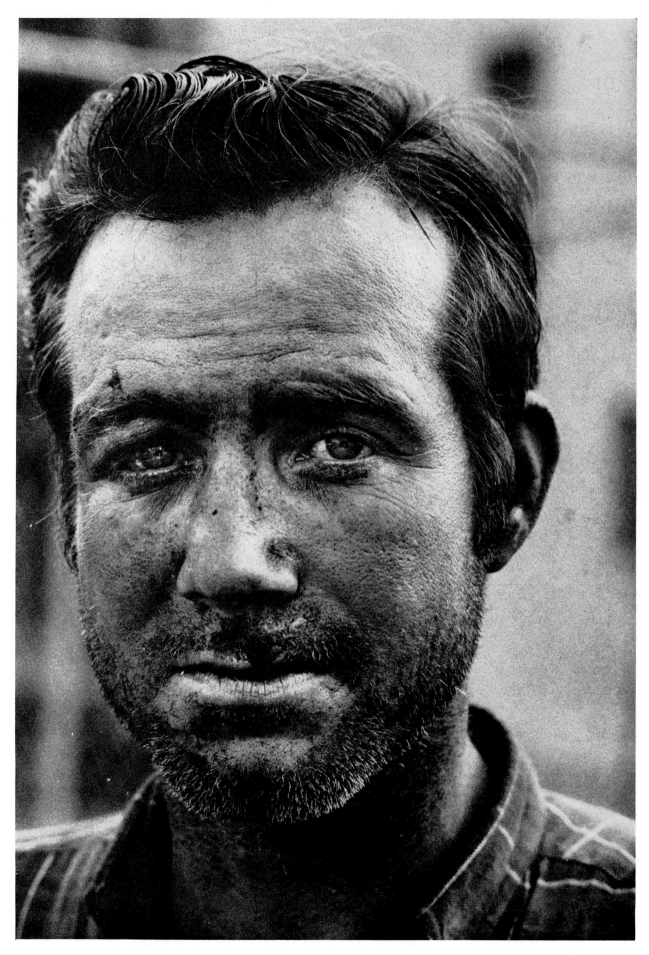

O. TSESARSKY

WILLIAM THORNTON

GABE CARPAY

STAN WEINER

AUL CARTER

O. TSESARSKY ▶

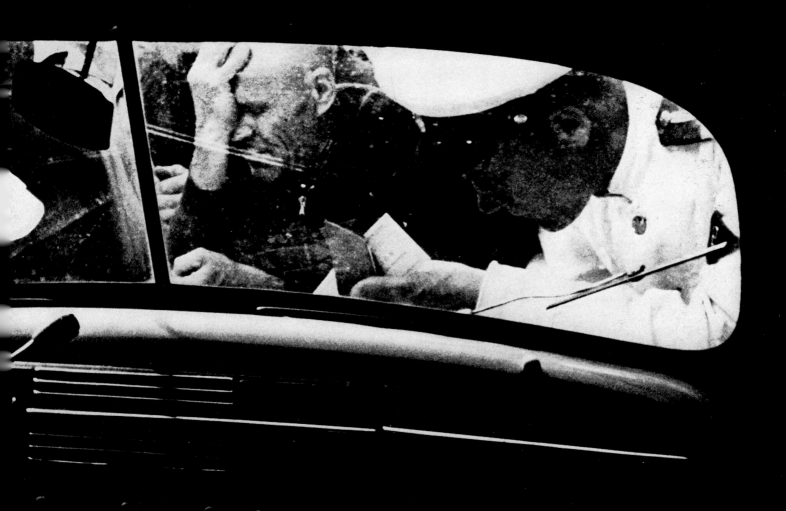

BOB DAVIS

V. LUKUS

EDOUARD BOUBAT

DAVID HURN

PETER TURNER

MICHAEL BARNET

BOB DAVIS

EDOUARD BOUBAT ▶

JOAQUIN CORTEZ

ERIC LOCKRAI

STUART WINDSOR

◀LARRY HERMAN

VAL PERRIN

66

E S Adams

A Portsmouth born photographer who has made his home in Uganda, where his professional life has been spent working for the Uganda Electricity Board, the *Uganda Argus* and the Uganda Ministry of Information.

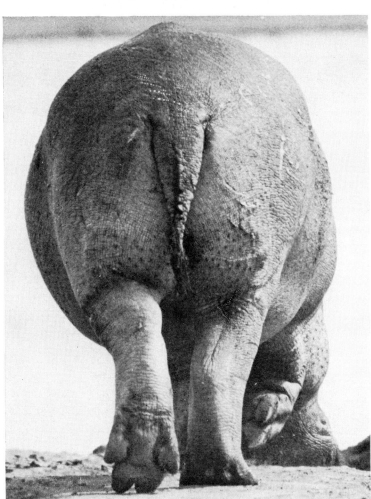

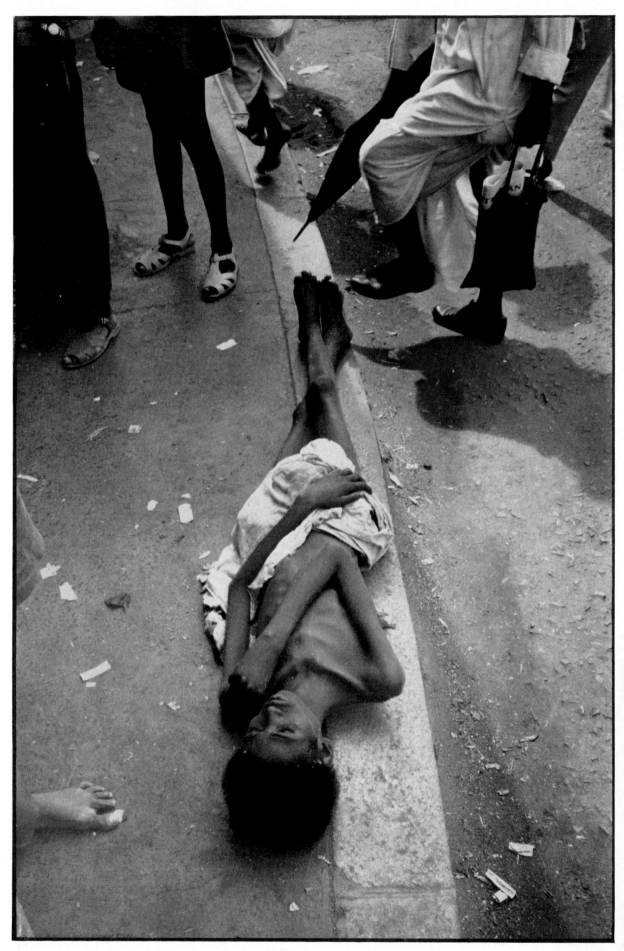

MARK EDWARDS

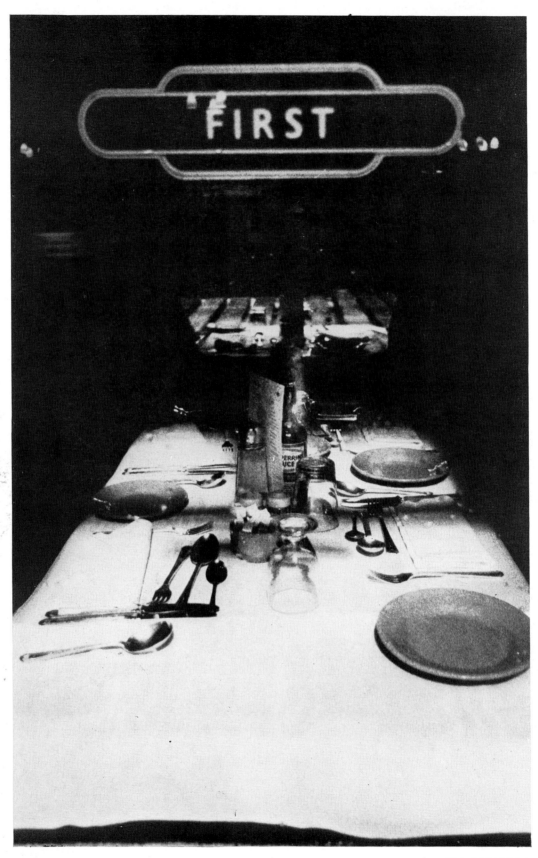

◀ O. MACAROV

JIM ARNOULD

Istvan Korda Kovacs

The work of Istvan Korda Kovacs has already been shown in the Annual as well as in the *British Journal of Photography*. Coming to London to study cinematography, he was awarded the diploma in the art and technique of film making at the London School of Film Technique. It was whilst he was in London that his still photography work became known in this country and in March 1969 he was photographer of the month at Kodak House. Hungarian by birth, Kovacs has spent a great deal of time in Norway where he now lives and is unusual in that he is working at the same time in still and movie photography. In movie, he has produced a number of documentaries for TV and in still photography his special interest has been the photography of sculpture as well as other art subjects. His one-man show in Oslo entitled 'Photo-impressions of Gustav Vigeland's Sculpture' brought him in contact with Arnold Haukeland, the most famous present day contemporary Norwegian sculptor. The result is a book on Haukeland's work extensively illustrated by Istvan Kovacs. He also held a joint exhibition with Haukeland showing the original sculpture of which Kovacs' experimental photography was based. In October 1970 sections of the Vigeland and Haukeland exhibitions were shown at the Institute of Contemporary Arts Gallery in London, this led to a commission to photograph Dame Barbara Hepworth in St Ives for a Norwegian magazine. Kovacs is currently working on a photographic exhibition about Hepworth's sculpture for the Sonja-Henie Art Centre in Oslo and at the same time he will be exhibiting a fresh genre of his own work which includes a novel approach to the photography of the human body. Some of this work showing the possibilities of photographic-sculpture is shown here.

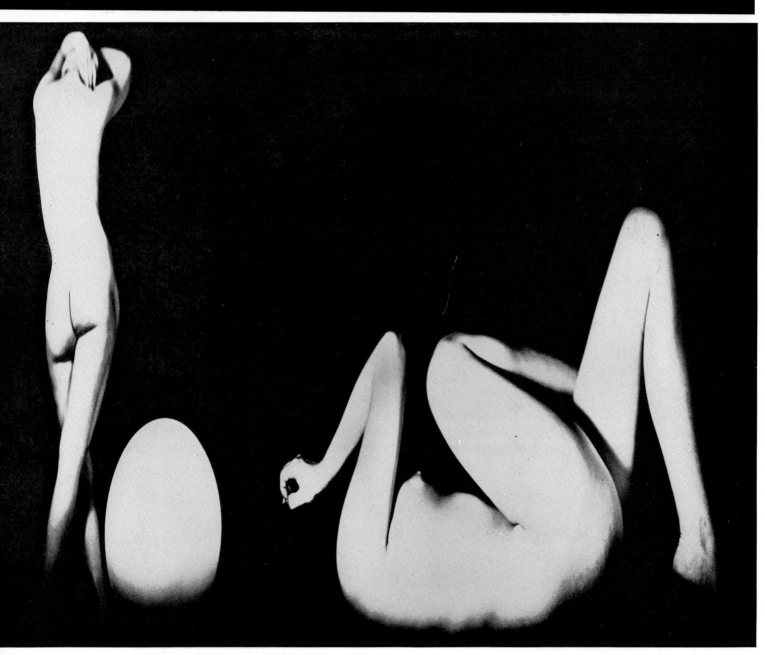

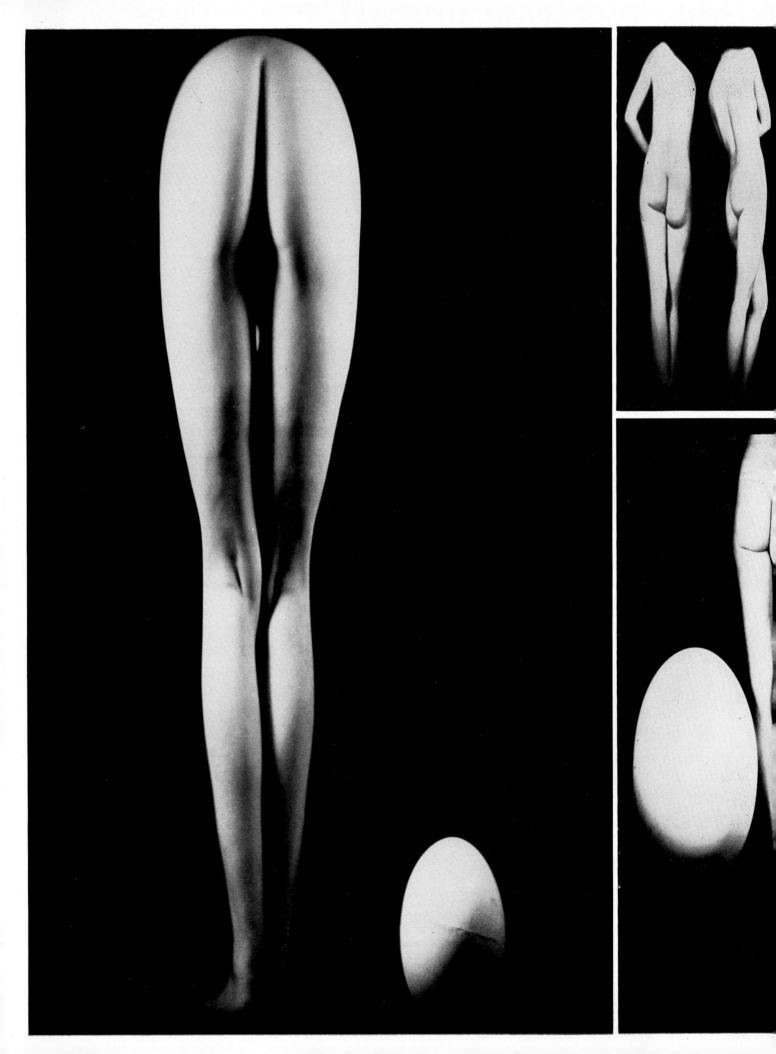

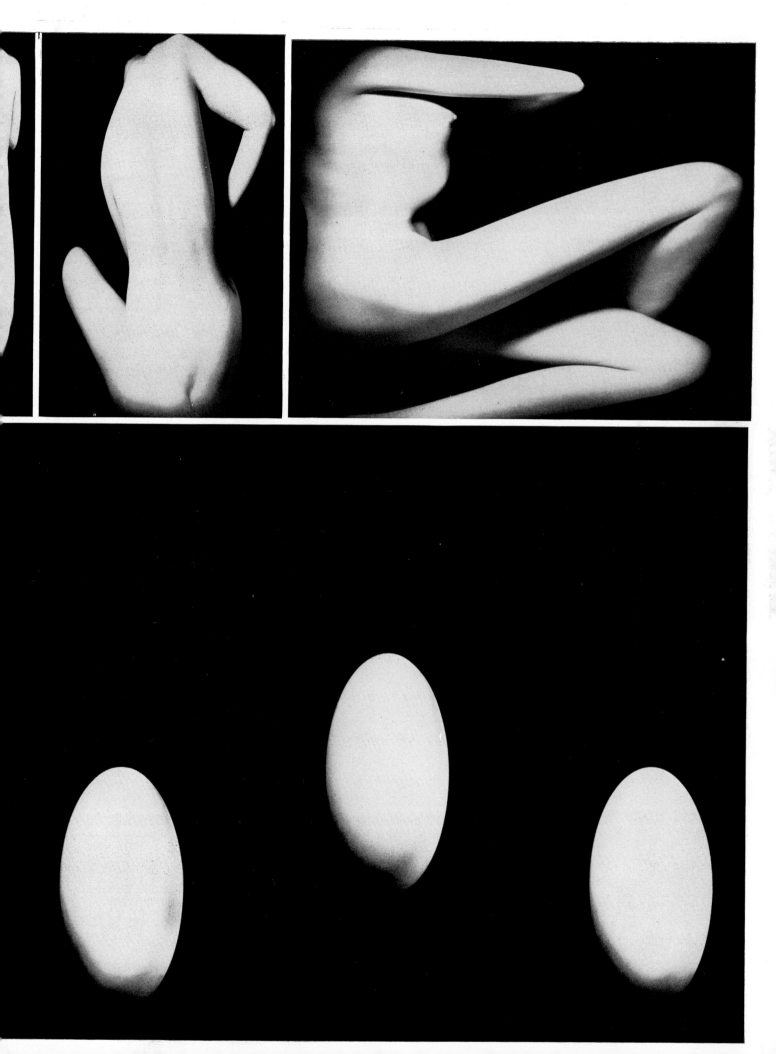

PEDRO LUIS RAOTA

PEDRO LUIS RAOTA

LANCE BROWN

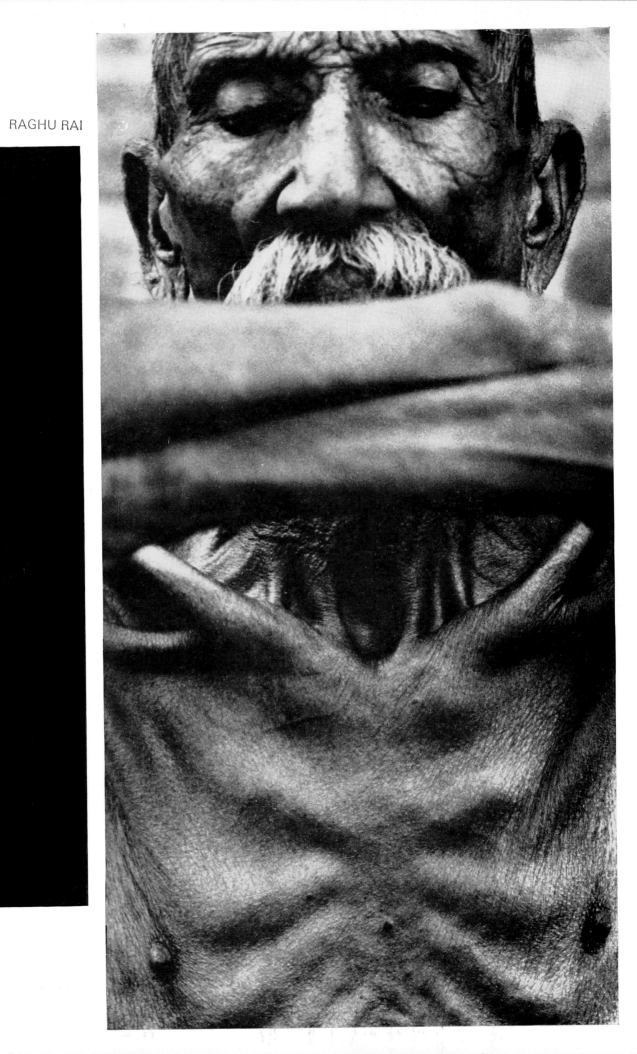

PETER LARSEN

VAL PERRIN

RICHARD & SALLY GREENHILL

DAVID NEWELL SMITH

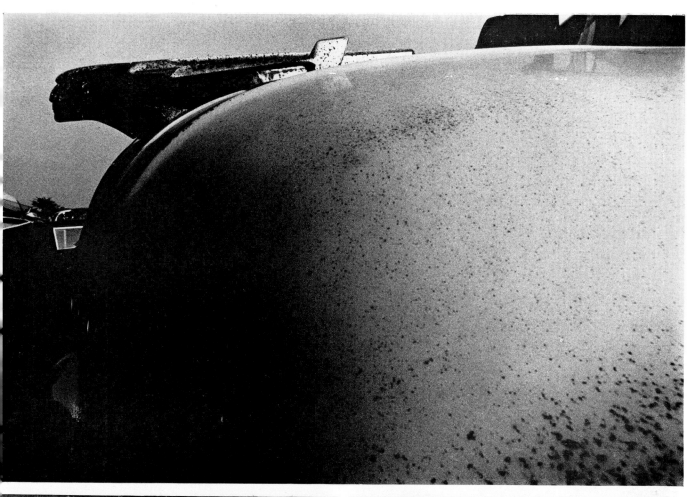

BARRIE WARD

THOMAS HÖPKER

A freelance photographer, Bryn Campbell FIIP, HonFRPS, has worked for the *Observer* for the past eight years, two of which were spent as Picture Editor. Also, as he was prior to this Editor of *Cameras*, Assistant Editor of the 'BJ', and first Picture Editor of the enlarged 'BJ' Annual in 1964, he can claim to have full experience of both sides of the fence—photographer and editor. In addition to assignments for the *Observer*, he now finds time to lecture and participate in the work of the IIP and RPS.

Below: Rail transport was free for the three days up to and including the funeral and thousands of people swarmed all over the trains into Cairo, half of them going back out again for the ride and then in again. This train was travelling at about 50 mph.

Right: Every available space was taken on the day of the funeral, people clinging to lamposts, bus

shelters, trees, unfinished build

Below right: One child nonchala

Over page: Arnold Palmer sinki
Piccadilly Match-Play Champio

Bryn Campbell

lding and even sitting on the tram cables.

oint of boredom in the midst of the mass hysteria.

utt which helped to clinch his victory in the final of the
nst Peter Thomson of Australia.

BRYN CAMPBELL

SRDJA DJUKANOVIC

MEIRA HAND

PATRICK WARD

RENE BURRI

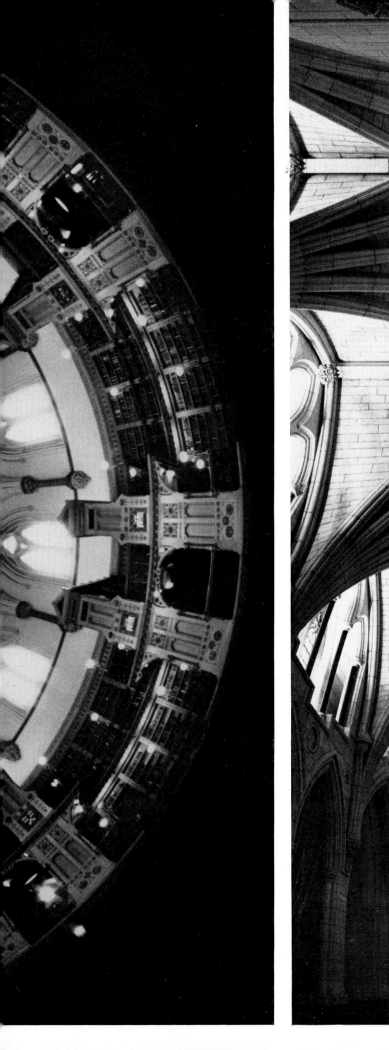

JACQUES-HENRI LARTIGUE

MICHAEL PETO   PEDRO LUIS RAOTA

RENE BURRI

TONY McGRATH

JOHN DONAT

◀ JOHN DONAT

JOHN WALSH

ALEX LEVAC

GEOFF HOWARD

Courtesy of Vogue

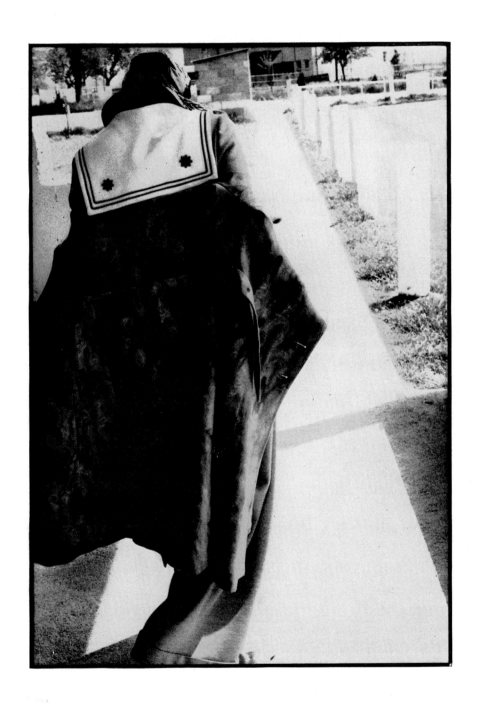

SUSAN BEIHOFFER

MARY ELLEN MARK

MARY ELLEN MARK

MARY ELLEN MARK   JOHN GOLDBLATT▶

FEATURE ARTICLES

A Compendium of Photographic History-Part 4

As reflected in the pages of the British Journal of Photography Almanacs 1911 to 1920

By Stanley W Bowler FRPS DGPh

Those who may have read the previous notes in this series may be interested to compare the physical characteristics of the Almanacs already reviewed with those about to be considered. Whereas 31in of shelf space were required to house the volumes published between 1900 and 1910, only 23in is needed for those in the 1911 to 1920 period—of these, slightly more than half the space is occupied by the first four years of the decade. The 'fat years' were coming to an end and the 'lean years' were beginning. In addition, the four years of the First World War—1914 to 1918—come into this contribution, although the volumes affected are those for 1915–1919.

The first volume is probably the most important for it is the *Jubilee Issue* of 1911, again edited by George E. Brown, FIC. The publishers' library copy is somewhat dilapidated from frequent reference to it, but it is embellished with gilt edges to the pages. The Editor's own contribution not unnaturally deals with 'The Story of the British Journal Almanac' and his first illustration is a line block of the original 'Photographic Almanac 1860'—in his text it is recorded that the *only known copy* is that in the British Museum. A facsimile of this Almanac was reproduced on page 122 of the 1969 edition of the *BJ Annual* . . . a small number of these photographic reproductions were made subsequently and are either in private hands or in national libraries.

At this point an impossible task emerges—how can one further précis fifty years of photographic history that was at that time already admirably done by an editor of the greatest eminence? For the research worker only the original material is valid. On a purely personal note, it was not until more than twenty years later that the present writer submitted his first contribution to him. To those who followed him he was a legend, to those who worked with him he was at one and the same time a hard, but sympathetic, task-master—demanding impeccable English and accurately researched material, written precisely to the length demanded and with 'copy' delivered on time and regularly. His ethical standards were high and woe betide anyone who over-stepped the bounds of professional propriety.

The editorial contribution to which reference has been made is a masterly one, concise in its coverage of the first fifty years of both the *Journal* and the *Almanac*. There are some interesting portraits of the personalities involved in the history of the publications up to 1911. He, George Brown, includes himself in the survey and refers to his privilege to superintend and to the reforms which had been made up to that time. He continued in office until 1934, when (after a short break with two other joint editors) in 1937 Arthur J. Dalladay, became the longest serving editor of all in the history of the *Almanac*. Brown was not unaware of the commercial aspect of publication and paid due regard to those who were concerned with this side of the business. There is an illustration, on p 489, of the premises at 24 Wellington Street, from which address the weekly *Journal* and the *Annual* are still published.

The *Epitome of Progress* takes pride of place and in the first section *Events of the Year* are detailed, including exhibitions, conferences and society functions; the second section deals with apparatus and equipment—there is a line illustration of the use of Welsbach incandescent gas-mantles for indoor portraiture (p 498) and a note about the extraction of heat by ventilators—present-day architects of office and other buildings please copy.

Section III has as its heading 'Photographing Various Subjects' and is eminently practical in its approach; studio design and lighting is stressed as are the methods for lighting control, including yet again references to umbrella lights . . . then we come to the more technical aspects of the art and science of photography of that time in IV 'Negative Processes' and V 'Printing Processes' followed by VI 'Colour Photography'. 'Recent Novelties in Apparatus, occupies the pages from 635 up to 719. The new still cameras are primarily of interest for style and date and nothing very remarkable appears to have been noted. On the other hand, in the introduction to the 'N-S' Cinematograph apparatus there is a reference to the newly-established firm as 'the fusion of the commercial direction of Mr James A. Sinclair and the genius in mechanics of Mr A.S. Newman'. Nowhere in this notice is there any reference to the actual gauge of the equipments discussed, camera, printer *and* perforator, although we now know it to have been nominal 35mm. The word 'nominal' is used deliberately because it may be inferred from the text where it is stated that Mr Newman's apparatus takes account of variations in width and pitch of perforations, and changes in length of negative and positive in processing.

In this issue, too, there are several references to light sources for projection including gas, with special mantles, acetylene, Nernst lamps, the author's first enlargements were made on an antiquated version of this fiendish device which had first to be warmed-up by flambée-ing it with methylated spirits, and a variety of electric arc-lamps. Projection lanterns also come in for their fair share of attention and that offered by Marion and Company Limited, the 'Soho Science Lantern' foreshadows the current interest in visual-aids, since with its micro-projection and other accessories it must have been a very versatile piece of apparatus.

The formulary and tabulated technical data section is much bigger than the new equipment section as it occupies the remainder of the editorial pages from 720 to 906. The advertisement pages are as interesting as ever, an invaluable reference source for photographic and motion-picture historians and collectors . . . The Bausch & Lomb Optical Company, then in Thavies Inn at Holborn Circus, London, EC, also offer a combination projection lantern, 'The Universal Balopticon' suitable for Class demonstration and College use. The Sheffield Photo Company mentions, in addition to its Home Cinematograph, at £5 15s 0d, SPC *Non-flam* films in 20 and 50ft lengths at 10s 6d and 21s. The advertisement pages are still international in character.

The 1912 volume is slightly bigger than that for 1911—1436 pages as against 1348. Once again the advertisement pages preponderate but, with all due respect to the distinguished authors and contributors of that time, they are of especial interest in indicating current trends in equipment of the period. The formulae section is again enlarged and a new one introduced called 'How To Do It' which is essentially practical in character.

Lantern-slide Making is the Editor's contribution and he chose this subject because he felt that, as far as exhibitions were concerned, public interest in prints was waning, there was a surfeit of them and the lay Press displayed aloofness . . . he concluded his first paragraph with 'those engaged in the task of giving the semblances of life to the dry bones of pictorial photography'. Hard words indeed, and yet prophetic of the present-day preoccupation with slides, although the format and the change from black-and-white to colour has taken place. In thirty pages, illustrated with line diagrams and supplemented with a variety of developers for cold, warm and coloured tones, George E. Brown shows what could be done by the really enthusiastic slide-maker of the time.

C.H. Hewitt FRPS discusses 'Indoor and Outdoor At Home Portraiture' and there are inset eight pages of half-tone pictures clearly identified as '*Illustrations to Article*'. The use of what would now be referred to as 'single-light technique' ie generally a window, with suitable reflectors, is explained. The use, too, of a wood strip extending forward of the lens and draped with the focusing-cloth as a lens-hood also indicates that the need to avoid stray light entering the lens was appreciated.

In the 'Obituary of the Year' is recorded the death, at 72, of M. Antoine Lumière on 16 April 1911—he was the founder of the company at Lyons (France) bearing his name. His two sons, Louis and Auguste Lumière, are perhaps better known because of their practical association with the development of the cinematograph, but the name of the company is also associated with the colour processes which were also to become historically interesting to still photographers.

Hydraulic camera pedestals, usually referred to as dollies, are generally considered to be very modern yet, once again, we find such a piece of equipment advertised as long ago as 1912. In this instance it is the *Graflex Studio Camera Stand*, sold by Kodak Limited from their Kingsway address. It is a massive piece of machinery with a vertical traverse of 18in and a minimum operating height of 2ft. Ball-bearing castors facilitate its movement about the studio. At £26 it was obviously a 'good buy', but, even so, dentists and barbers had been using the same basic pedestal for their chairs for some years.

The processing data and tabular information section took up rather less space than in previous years (pp 761–910) owing to the fact that some data and tables had been omitted, but the reader was still provided with references to prior information and earlier material should he have wished to look it up.

Advertisers appeared to be less squeamish in those days about the use of what is now known as 'knocking copy'—a case in point was that for the *Kinora* system of *Motion Photography for Amateurs* by Bond's Limited of 138 New Bond Street, London, W. Thirty pages are devoted to extolling the virtues of Kinora and the way in which the amateur could outshine artistically the makers of news-pictures which one critic had described as 'more or less violently out-of-focus, with a distressing shakiness and flicker'. The 'copy-writing' is

lyrical—and the lady-of-the-house was obviously well in mind in the description of the Model No. 1, which was 'Operated by clockwork, is made of mahogany, has three lenses, and is richly embellished with gilt carving. It is mounted on an inlaid mahogany pedestal to contain twenty Kinora reels'. Such a device would obviously not have been out of place in the most elegant drawing-room.

Other photographic magazines were advertised in the *Almanac* pages and in this particular edition were included the *Amateur Photographer*, edited by F.J. Mortimer FRPS, *Abel's Photographic Weekly* of Cleveland, Ohio and *Camera Craft* of San Francisco, USA.

The *Almanac* for 1913 is slightly bigger than that for 1912 as it contains 1448 pages and is about $2\frac{3}{4}$in thick. It is also interesting because it includes quite a lot of colour, mainly in the advertising pages. In fact, in the Preface, dated 25 October 1912, the Editor, George E. Brown, refers to two notable pieces of work—(i) the frontispiece as an example of machine photogravure by Messrs Vandyck Printers Limited of Bristol printed on a continuous reel of paper at a rate of 8000 copies per hour, and (ii) the inclusion in the text pages (between pp 778 and 779) of a reproduction of an Autochrome by Oskar Trinkler of the Carl Zeiss staff using a Zeiss $6\frac{1}{2}$in f/6·3 Tessar—the exposure time was 4sec in diffused light at 5.30pm on a July afternoon and the subject was an open-air drama.

The Editor's main contribution is about darkrooms, their fitting out, illumination and so on, both permanent and temporary. The use of a bathroom is, not unnaturally, referred to and here I must take issue with the author for he suggests that a board should be placed on the top of the bath to provide a processing bench. This really is impractical—the recommendation has been repeated in the literature on many occasions, but I suspect that it has been suggested by those who have access to a conventional darkroom and who wished to try to be helpful to others less fortunate. Admittedly it *will* work but it is a most inconvenient solution to the problem of finding processing space. First of all, the level of the bath rim is far too low for anyone but a dwarf and one cannot sit comfortably by a bath because there is nowhere to put one's knees or feet. A 'bath' bench *must* be raised by about a foot or so (from, say, 22in to 34–36in) by means of cross battens or a sub-staging to make it tolerably usable.

The second major contribution is by Captain Owen Wheeler FRPS about 'Practical Methods of Telephotography' and the eight pages of inset moderately good quality half-tone pictures are included here. The paper used is, of course, rather better than that upon which the rest of the editorial matter is printed.

In the *Epitome of Progress* under the *Business* heading it was reported that The Eastman Kodak Company had purchased Wratten and Wainwright of Croydon and that Dr C.E.K. Mees, previously a director of W&W, had become the head of a new research laboratory of the E.K. Company at Rochester. This was originally reported in the *BJ* in the issue dated 23 February 1912 on page 133.

In this particular issue the *Epitome of Progress* is not especially stimulating as it seems to be concerned rather too much with what might be termed gadgets, but in Section III—Photographing various subjects, there is what is believed to be the first reference to the patented use of projected backgrounds, using a 'powerful projector apparatus' and a translucent screen behind the sitter, for a single combination exposure.

In the new apparatus section there are two items which merit reference: the first of these is the Sanger–Shepherd Density-meter which was one of the simplest and yet surprisingly accurate of the first densitometers. It was about the size of a cigar box and did not look unlike one; through the eyepiece two semi-circular patches were seen—one representing the density to be measured and the other a portion of the graduated continuous wedge which was slid from left-to-right, or vice versa. When a match was obtained the density was read off the calibrated wedge, fairly accurately, simply and cheaply.

The second item was the introduction of the folding *Vest-pocket Kodak;* a roll-film camera taking eight exposures $2\frac{1}{2} \times 1\frac{3}{8}$ in. At that time it cost just thirty bob and the film was 10d. Britain will now having changed to decimal instead of Imperial currency, the figures had better be amended to £1.50 and 4p respectively.

For many people the year 1914 is a reminder only of the start of the First World War, but the *Almanac* for that year was fatter than ever, only four pages short of 1500, 3in thick

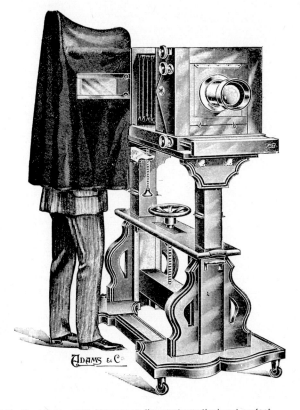

Advertised in the 1915 Almanac as the most practical and perfect portraiture camera ever built, the Adams Studio Minex, cost £73.10s, complete with 16in F/4 Ross portrait lens.

and weighed almost $3\frac{1}{2}$lb. It would have been published about the beginning of the year, bearing as it does an editorial date-line of 24 October 1913, and was thus unaffected by the events of 1914 itself.

In addition to providing the first contribution about 'Lens

Facts for Amateurs' the Editor introduces two new features in this edition; the first was a glossary of photographic terms (pp 885–894) and the second the equivalents in German, French and Italian of the chief photographic terms. He gave the reason for the inclusion of the latter as 'a help to those referring to foreign photographic books and periodicals as well as to foreign readers of the *Almanac*'. The second article was again by C.H. Hewitt FRPS who dealt with 'Exposure and Development' and a dozen pages of half-tone pictures of both negatives and positives were inset. More half-tone illustrations were used on the rest of the text pages, but line diagrams and sketches were still much in evidence.

First among the notes about new equipment is one on the Adams Studio Reflex Camera, including what must have been one of the earliest back-of-camera control systems as well as a virtually all-enveloping focusing-cloth so that the sitter would not be upset by the photographer's mechanical activities. The operator was also provided with a tinted window in his shroud so that he could more easily assess the photographic result. Motion-picture equipment also began to receive more notice (for example, the *Ensign* daylight-loading cinematograph camera, sold by Houghtons Limited of High Holborn, London, WC), although the battle of the gauges had already started. Houghtons also offered the *Pathéscope Home Cinematograph* and the text about it refers to 'The film is of a somewhat narrower width than that in standard machines . . .' It also had a small over-run metallic filament lamp powered by a built-in hand-turned magneto. From the description, although the film-width is not stated, this is fairly certainly the Pathéscope KOK using 28mm film stock. (The trade-name KOK is a play on the word *coq*, for the company's trade-mark is a cockerel.)

According to the Kodak Museum catalogue, this KOK 28mm projector dates from 1912, so that it is perhaps not very surprising to find a few pages further on in this 1914 *Almanac* a note about the *Tress Home Cinematograph Projector* supplied by a company of the same name from 4 Rathbone Place, London, W which also had a 'little dynamo geared with the handle of the machine . . . a small metallic filament lamp . . . slightly over-run'. But the key-line in the reference is 'The projector has the very positive advantage of taking the standard size of film . . .' The 'standard' mentioned was, of course, 35mm width.

Most of the still cameras mentioned in this issue appear to have conformed to fairly conventional designs, either as box-form single-lens reflex or folding types, with Newman's 'trellis' or lazy-tongs design taking pride of place for stabilising the front lens panel.

George E. Brown's editorial in the 1915 *Almanac* bears the date 3 December 1914; in it he first refers to the fact that this fifty-fourth volume was an increased issue of 30,000 copies (it was, however, reduced in size by about a third to 1068 pages), to 'the present disastrous European War' and, lastly, to 'When the war is ended, as we all hope it may be before the next *Almanac* is issued, we may expect to see the British photographic trade further extended and strengthened in all the great markets of the world'. As it happened, neither the hope nor the expectation was fulfilled.

One of the advertisers was quick off the mark to support the Editor's idea, for Butler and Tanner, Printers of Frome, took four pages, with the key-line on the first of them 'Wake Up

England' and the second, third and fourth appealing to advertisers in English, French and Russian respectively 'To Capture German Trade'. It was noted, too, that 'We have ample supplies of materials . . .'

The patriotic flavour is also to be found in many of the other announcements with the phrases 'British Made', 'All British', 'British Capital and Labour', 'Printed in London *entirely by* British Machinery and experienced British Staff'. Nevertheless, as the Editor also pointed out, with very few exceptions, British companies did support very well indeed this first *Almanac* of the war years. American and French products were listed and Gevaert Limited, through its then Managing Director, Chas J. Miller stated that it was 'the British Branch of an entirely Belgian firm whose head offices are at Antwerp'.

The principal contributions were on 'Modern Methods of Enlarging' by the Editor and 'Photography with the Microscope' by Dr Duncan J. Reid MB, with eight pages of inset half-tone illustrations. Next, in Obituary of the Year, the deaths of several famous men were recorded with suitable details of their achievements. Sir Joseph Swan (d 27 May 1914), who partnered the company of Mawson & Swan Limited, dry-plate makers of Newcastle-on-Tyne, will be remembered for his work on collodion and carbon printing. B.J. Edwards (d 24 May 1914) was another manufacturer of dry-plates and originated the mercuric-iodide method of intensifying negatives. George Hare (d 21 November 1913) was a pioneer camera maker, having served an apprenticeship to his father in joinery in Yorkshire. Other deaths briefly noted include those of Monsieur Bertillon, inventor of the criminal identification system bearing his name and Gustav Cramer, another dry-plate manufacturer—but in this instance in St Louis, USA.

Reference has been made in previous parts of this historical compendium about the way in which old 'inventions' keep re-appearing. In the 1915 *Epitome of Progress* in Section II dealing with Apparatus and Equipment there is a reference to and an illustration of a lens mount devised by The Thornton Pickard Manufacturing Company Limited, A.G. Pickard and F. Slinger. The English Patent Number was 2231 of 1913 and it was reviewed in the *BJ* in the issue dated 3 April 1914 on p 271. The lens mount consists of a ball-and-socket housing within which the lens is fixed so that it may be swung or tilted in all directions. A mounting very similar in conception was shown at photokina 1968 under the name *Scheimpflug Varioflex* and referred to in detail in the issue of the *BJ* dated 7 March 1969 in 'Technical Digest' on p 237—the manufacturer being Firma Atzmueller & Rendl, of A-4042 LINZ/Donau, Postfach 29, Austria. It is understood that, since then, another variant has also appeared. About fifty years or so seems to be the average time-lapse between first and second phases.

In 'Recent Novelties in Apparatus' the designs of cameras again appear to be more or less stabilised; W. Watson and Sons Limited, of 313 High Holborn, London, WC, introduced the *Mite* vest-pocket camera fitted with a focal-plane shutter and Houghtons Limited also introduced a De Luxe version of their *Ensignette* folding camera. But the most attention seems to have been devoted to sources of artificial light, where reference is made to the new *Osram* metallic-filament lamps of higher efficiency than had previously been obtainable, as well as a multiplicity of flash-lamps and of arc lamps. Staley

and Company of Thavies Inn, London, EC, offered a *Junior Britisher Reflex* camera, ¼-plate size with an f/4·5 Aldis lens.

The highlight of the section is a patriotic photographic ring, made in 9 carat gold, within which a miniature portrait may be placed and on the outside of which there is enamelled in colours a Union Jack. Price 10s 9d.

Judging by the issue of 1916 the War seems to have had little effect for the number of pages was only reduced to 984: the editorial was dated 4 December 1915 and it was stated that the war would have lasted a year and a half without (at the time of writing) any victory of military decisiveness having been obtained on either side, apart from Great Britain's mastery of the sea, by the time it reached the reader. There are some philosophical considerations of the lack of raw materials and deficiencies in labour but the photographic industry did not appear to have been materially discommoded. However, instead of a review of new introductions of photographic equipment, in pp 507 to 586 it was considered more appropriate to list a survey of the production of requisites for photography. The Editor pointed out that, in reading that survey, it would show that 'already in several important respects we are rendering ourselves independent of German supplies'.

But, even at this time, it was not just equipment and materials which mattered and already the British film industry was being supplanted by the American . . . London and Brighton were to give way to Hollywood in due course, and at least a half-century was to pass before Europe again became important in this field and British studios once more take the lead in technical efficiency.

There is only one major contribution and that is by George E. Brown, the Editor, dealing with 'Practical Notes on Printing Processes'—it is somewhat heavy going and there are no illustrations*. That photography could contribute something to the war effort is indicated by the first General note in the *Epitome of Progress* where it is stated that 'Under the auspices of the YMCA the services of amateur and professional photographers have been largely organised for the purpose of sending to soldiers and sailors engaged in the war at home and abroad photographs of their folk at home'·

The survey of British resources is now, of course, only of prime interest to historians since it provides not only a long

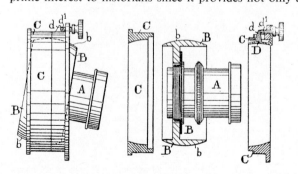

L to R: Thornton Pickard perspective control lens.
Voigtländer hand camera.
Pathéscope Home Cinematograph.

list of manufacturers of equipment and materials and their

* *In fact, in this issue, for the first time in many years, there are relatively few illustrations, apart from the frontispiece in Vandyck photogravure, and a number of line drawings and diagrams.*

addresses at that time but also their products and the trade-names which they used. There is virtually no reference whatever to the use of photography, or of motion-pictures, in the war effort—perhaps due to considerations of national security. Only in the notes about Houghtons Limited is there a slightly petulant comment about 'the demands upon the factory itself in the supply of goods for various Government departments. It will be understood that with such insistent claims upon their resources Messrs Houghtons have consequently been unable to maintain the supply of, etc. . . .' In retrospect, and with a second World War within more recent memory, one might comment "What a pity!" In the entry for the Thornton-Pickard Manufacturing Company Limited there is no reference whatever to the part which they played in supplying photographic equipment to the Armed forces.

But, in all fairness, it should be realised that the armed forces themselves had not, at that time, wakened up to the fact that aerial (or any other type, for that matter) photography could be of very much use in the waging of a war.

The advertisement pages generally seem completely aloof from the conflict, although Rajar Limited of Mobberley in Cheshire, in an eight-page inset, with a leading illustration entitled 'His Picture', in a centre-spread tear at the heartstrings with references to brave lads in khaki and the gentler sex left behind, etc. and so on.

The *Almanac* continued to shrink in size in the number of pages and in 1917 it was down to 780 pages and only about 1¾in in thickness. The advertisements do not appear to have diminished very much and are as glossy as ever, but the Editor draws attention to the fact that the *Almanac* is at last feeling the pinch . . . not only was it reduced in size but the edition contracted from 30,000 copies to 20,000 due to restrictions in the supply of paper and its cost. He concluded with the sentence 'Again, in times of "nothing-as-usual" we would claim the indulgence of our readers, in the hope and belief that before another *Almanac* is ready Europe will have witnessed the defeat of the Prussian military caste.' Date line—4 December 1916.

It would seem that the Editor was in some difficulty in choosing a subject for his principal contribution and selected 'Chemical Notes for Photographers'. Again there were no

illustrations and the article is not particularly inspiring, merely serving to tidy up some misconceptions and give the average reader an insight into the subject as a useful exercise rather than a stimulating discussion.

The *Obituary of the Year* contained one most important

name, that of Vero C. Driffield (d 14 November 1915), the famous partner of Dr Ferdinand Hurter, whose joint photographic researches were collated in the memorial volume published by The Royal Photographic Society and edited by W.B. Ferguson KC, MA(Oxon), FIC, HonFRPS, in 1920. Another famous name was that of Professor Silvanus P. Thompson, FRS (d 12 June 1916) who, although primarily interested in electricity, had delivered the Traill-Taylor Memorial Lecture to the RPS in 1901 on the subject of *Zonal Aberration*, delighting his audiences with a series of fascinating experimental demonstrations. He also gave a series of children's lectures at The Royal Institution.

For the second year in succession mechanical plate-rockers take pride of place in the Apparatus and Equipment section of the *Epitome of Progress*, even including one with an eccentric electric-motor powered drive. The line illustrations to this and other articles in this section are meagre and suggest that there was a dearth of material available. Finally, Cinematography, as in previous issues, gets short shrift with the comment 'Space will not permit of reference to the numerous patents for cinematograph cameras, projectors and animated photography in monochrome and natural colours'. The reader is referred to the columns of the *BJ* for the specifications.

At pp 418–419 there is inset a specimen print of Vitégas (2a)* velvet paper of a male portrait which is still in excellent condition despite its relatively great age. It is on double-weight paper.

Among the advertising pages there is a newcomer in 'Boots the Chemists' . . . since that time, with the company's multitudinous branches, it has been claimed that, in effect it, operates one of the biggest chains of retail shops in the world dealing with photography. Even in 1917 600 *branches* was part of the advertising slogan. Boots offered not only its own exclusive models of equipment but also those of Kodak and a number of other munufacturers.

Patriotic slogans were becoming more forceful and in the highly-coloured first page of the Johnsons inset advertisement for chemicals there is a composite picture of guns firing and a busy factory with smoke pouring from its chimneys with the overlaid lettering 'British Manufacture, Britain's Defence'. The Modern Scenographie Company of Catford, London, SE made it plain that their backgrounds were painted in their own studios 'where **we do not employ alien enemies** in any capacity whatever'.

George E. Brown's editorial in the 1918 *Almanac*, dated 5 December 1917, makes quite clear the fact that the war really has had some effect. It is short enough to merit quoting it in full. 'The fourth war-time *Almanac* has been prepared under the stricter conditions of paper-rationing, which has further limited the number of its pages (*although still* 660 *pages*), both text and advertisement. Nevertheless it is believed that both sections fulfil the functions which the book has discharged for so many years. The one continues to provide photographers with information in daily need. The other now shows how the photographic trade of Great Britain has withstood the stress of three and a half years of war.

* *Vitégas was the trade-name for the gaslight emulsion produced by Kosmos Photographics Limited of Letchworth, Hertfordshire, and in the company's advertisement it was stated that their papers were 'British through and through'.*

'Particularly as regards the text, space has been saved by omitting items in the "Formulae" section which could well be spared; also by foregoing the inclusion of the list of Colonial photographic societies, from the majority of which, for self-evident reasons, particulars have not been forthcoming. Those secretaries who were able to answer our application will therefore understand why use could not be made of their replies. To them, and to all others who, in these difficult times, have contributed in any way to the volume, a sincere acknowledgement of indebtedness is here made.'

Between the lines of that editorial we can now read something of the difficulties which a war-time editor faced in trying to keep both a weekly and an annual publication in being. Arthur J. Dalladay was to face the same problems during the Second World War and to succeed in dealing with problems associated with enemies outside the country, only to be defeated by others within its borders following upon the cessation of hostilities when a printers' strike caused publication of the *BJ* to stop for a few weeks in common with other periodicals.

In his editorial contribution on 'Miscellanea of Negative

In the General section of the *Epitome of Progress* a warning note is sounded about the gradual increase in price of a dozen $\frac{1}{4}$-plates—in June 1913 they could be bought for a shilling; then they rose to 1s 3d, and again in March 1915 to 1s 6d. The third rise in price took place in February 1916, up to 1s 10d, and by 1 March 1916 the fourth rise in price took them to 2s 3d. Similar rises in price also took place in charges for developing and printing. Inflation was obviously on its way.

Among a variety of rather elementary contributions on photographic studio and workroom practice there is one which foreshadows processing-temperature control. An oil-lamp is set below the main part of the darkroom bench and above a slot cut in it there is a subsidiary metal duct through which the hot gases pass and on the top of which the developer, rinse and fixing dishes are placed. The author advises that when the desired temperature is reached the oil-lamp should be turned down low.

In their advertisements, both Johnsons and Kentmere obviously were anticipating the end of hostilities for the former has as its leading illustration a colour picture of

Making' George E. Brown refers to 'the process of marking time in almost every branch of camera work except that of photography from the air'. This is virtually the only hint we get in this period of the practical use of photography in the prosecution of the war. Yet again, no illustrations and very few of them in the rest of the text matter of this issue of the *Almanac*.

merchant ships and a biplane (although still with Royal Flying Corps red, white and blue roundels) moving away from a port—the caption is 'Johnson's Chemicals for Overseas', while Kentmere state that their products are 'The Best Papers for Overseas—as they keep good and free from discolouration for any time in any climate and do not frill'.

That their hopes were possibly to be fulfilled seemed likely since the *Preface* to the 1919 issue is dated 15 November 1918 . . . just four days after the formal cessation of hostilities. This issue again declined in size, although it still contained 644 pages. The Editor states that 'An armistice in March would have enabled us to have made the succeeding *Almanac* worthy of being the first to be published in peace. That task, however, must be reserved for the 1920 issue'.

In the advertising pages at the front half of the 1919 *Almanac* is one sponsored by Wellington and Ward Limited, with a factory at Elstree in Hertfordshire and showrooms at 101 High Holborn, London. These showrooms, between the wars, were to become a special venue for many different types of photographic exhibitions staged by Ilford Limited. First *Photography as an Art* is considered and then comes the first hint of the part which it played during the war years, for the next section is entitled *Photography as the Eyes of the Army*. There are two illustrations, one of which shows an RAF biplane bomber, taken by searchlight, and the other, an aerial photograph showing bombs bursting on a fort on the Palestine front. This seems very meagre recognition of the work which such pioneers as Arthur Kingston FBKS, FRPS, and others

and allied processes to trimming and mounting. While it is a useful record of the times it is not, with all due respect, very profound. To some extent this general tenor is reflected in the first note in the General section of the *Epitome of Progress* which refers to an Event of the Year 1917—the Traill-Taylor Memorial Lecture, the 20th in the series, entitled 'Some Minor Processes of Photography'. However, on 14 May 1918 W.B. Ferguson delivered the first Hurter and Driffield Memorial Lecture, so that all was not lost at this unhappy time.

Also recorded is the inaugural meeting of *The British Photographic Research Association*, on 11 June, presided over by Sir Joseph J. Thomson, President of The Royal Society. A few days later it was announced that *Photography and Focus* had been amalgamated with the *Amateur Photographer* and that the latter had been purchased from the original publishers Messrs Hazell, Watson and Viney by Messrs Iliffe and Sons Limited, with which latter company it has remained since.

By August 1918 the price of $\frac{1}{4}$-plates had risen to 3s 8d per dozen and it was noted that this was the fifth rise which had taken place during the war. Horror upon horrors! Once

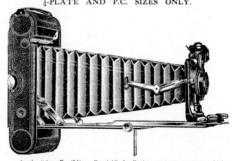

put in at Farnborough and similar places during that war. Those who achieve any sort of acclaim within fifty years of their actual contributions to new developments are indeed fortunate.

The principal article is that by the Editor entitled 'Photographic Definitions' and runs the gamut from the lens, through cameras and accessories, negatives, chemicals, prints

again, at the end of the section dealing with Printing Processes (V), *Cinematography* is, to some extent, shrugged off with the comment made in the previous issue that the numerous patents do not permit of reference to them and one is, therefore, obliged to go back to the weekly details published or abstracted in the *BJ*. Unless one has access to those weekly issues this is a most tantalising situation.

The Editor's hopes about the 1920 *Almanac* were fulfilled for it contained 912 pages—the first increase of almost 50% above that for 1919 and in his editorial George E. Brown expresses disappointment that it had not been possible, owing to 'circumstances of unrest in which the restoration of manufacture and commerce to their full measure of activity has been greatly impeded'. One or two features that had had to be dropped were reinstated, one or two new fresh items of contents were added and the edition was restored to its pre-war figure of 25,000. The preface was dated 15 November 1919—a little more than a year after the end of hostilities.

For the first time, on the page facing the contents, there was the *Biographical Note* which has been included in most *Almanacs* ever since. It refers to the formats of the editions up to that date and lists the eight editors who had presided over the years from 1861 until 1906, which was the time when George E. Brown took over from Thomas Bedding.

His editorial in this, the last edition to be considered in this particular decade, was entitled '*Beginners' Failures in Photography*'. In fifty-eight pages he dealt at great length with faults in negatives, bromide and self-toning papers. Two names stand out in the *Obituary* section—first C. Welbourne Piper, who was for a considerable number of years a member of the staff of the *BJ* and one of the leading investigators and writers who had taken the processes of photography as a field of study. He died on 4 March 1919. The other name is that of Sir William Crookes, who died on 4 April 1919 in his eighty-seventh year —an eminent chemist and physicist. A contribution to photographic processes, which was commonly attributed to Sir William, in the text books of the nineteenth century, was that of having been the first to use the light of burning magnesium for taking photographs. In January 1857 he became editor of what is now the *BJ*, but which was then issued as *The Liverpool and Manchester Photographic Journal*, although this editorship lasted only for about two years.

In the *Business* section of the *Epitome of Progress* it was announced that there had been a reduction in the price of ¼-plates from 3s 8d to 3s 0d so, as ¼-plates seemed then to be the criteria of value, photography was saved from disaster!

Lenses and Photographic Optics are dealt with in Section II . . . and in this section one obtains the first real information about the part which British designers played during the war years. Mention is made of such now-famous names as A. Taylor, H. Dennis Taylor, H. Lee, A. Warmisham (Taylor, Taylor & Hobson Limited) and J. Hasselkus (Ross Limited)— also recorded are the briefest details of the 20in f/5·6 and 36in f/6 lenses of Aldis Limited, used for making aerial photographs of Zeebrugge. The same group of companies provided similar types of lenses in the last War, when the name of Lionel Booth was especially associated with very long focal length lenses for high altitude reconnaisance work.

For what is believed to be the first time, in Section III of the *Epitome* under the heading of '*Photographing Various Subjects*' (and then not as the first item) we read of the *Williamson or F Type Aeroplane Camera* and of its successor the *Laws or L Camera*. The *LB* development of it had a completely replaceable focal-plane shutter unit. 'Laws', of course, was Major F.C.V. Laws, who was also to be closely associated with aerial photography during the Second World War, as was the Williamson Manufacturing Company Limited.

There is a considerable number of references to other articles, patent specifications and so on in the *BJ* itself during the latter war years in which one finds the names of such eminent men as Monsieur L.P. Clerc (in connexion with the French Army Aviation Service) as well as further notes about the activities of The Thornton-Pickard Manufacturing Company (which company it was stated was the largest producer of cameras for military aerial work) and more particularly the *Hythe gun camera* used for training air pilots in machine gunnery.

In Section VI dealing with *Colour Photography* there is a sub-section concerned with *Cinematography in Colours* and the first item refers to a 'Prism and Grid for Two-colour Photography' by D.F. Comstock and Technicolor Motion Corporation . . . this must be one of the first such references to Technicolor; most people regard this name as of relatively recent origin. F.E. Ives was at work with two-colour systems (red and green separation negatives), as was Aron Hamburger and L.F. Douglass. Six-colour cinematography, based on the *Kinemacolor* principle, was devised by J. Shaw.

The formulary and tables appeared to have been restored almost to their pre-war fullness and there is a useful reference to tabulations and so on which had been withdrawn in the interests of saving space.

The advertisement pages were still primarily British, although a number of American and French companies, as well as those from Belgium, Burma, Denmark and New Zealand contributed. Even the Army & Navy Co-operative Society Limited of Francis Street, Westminster, London, SW1 had its own Photographic and Lantern Department and offered such 'Special' items as a double-extension Roll-film Camera (¼-plate and P.C. sizes only) and a ¼-plate *Dwarf* single-lens reflex, in six pages of advertising.

One of the first automatic (that is, self-powered) motion-picture cameras was advertised in the 1920 *Almanac* (p 820) by Eracam Limited of 32 Gray's Inn Road, Holborn, London, WC1. It was the *Aeroscope*, invented by C. de Prosynski, in which the whole of the mechanism ran on compressed air, holding 300ft of 'standard' ie 35mm, film in interchangeable boxes so that it could be loaded and un-loaded in daylight . . . all adjustments made from outside the camera. The pumping system had been superseded by charging from pocket cylinders.

Although, at this time, we are considering equipment and materials which were in vogue just over half-a-century ago it is surprising how many of the trade-names and marks seem somehow still to be quite fresh in one's memory. In point of fact, of course, many names then famous still exist today although there have been some losses and many amalgamations of smaller companies into bigger concerns which, in turn have been swallowed up into intercontinental organisations. On a nostalgic note, one remembers the *Popular Pressman* ¼-plate reflex (probably even by then slightly secondhand), with a Ross/Xpres f/4·5 lens wide open, which one borrowed for the school's sports day and used Wellington *Anti-screen* plates with a top speed of 400H&D. The enlargements would probaly have been made on Illingworth's *Platino-Matt Smooth* paper using a horizontal *Lancaster* enlarger and a *Nernst* lamp to which reference has already been made. Happy days!

The Photographer and the Natural World
Robert McClelland

Introduction

The history of photography as a medium of expression can be understood in terms of the interaction of two basic motivations—the synthetic approach depends upon the *creation* of a visual statement which has been radically altered from the scene as presented in reality; the analytical approach relies upon the photographer's ability to *select* and record a significant visual event without interference, thereby presenting an aspect of reality for our contemplation. The former approach to photography lies closely akin to other visual media in that the resulting work is an expression of the photographer's inner-self and has little bearing upon the outside world as seen. The latter, analytical approach is characterised by a uniqueness of means, and although a large proportion of it is occupied by photojournalism there is a growing tendency to adopt such an approach by workers for whom photography is primarily a medium of aesthetic expression. This movement of analytical or 'pure' photography has been in existence for many years and could hardly be described as an innovation, but in these times when the nature of reality is regularly in question it has gained particular significance as a vehicle for the prescription of intuitional values relating to the world.

Within the confines of a short essay it would be futile to attempt to give due regard to all the manifestations of such an approach, and this discussion is restricted to a consideration of one of the dominant tendencies—the interpretation of the natural world.

Nature and reality

Nature—by which is meant the physical power causing the phenomena of the material world—has always been a source of fascination to speculative minds. Scientists, philosophers and artists of all kinds have consistently found inspiration in the natural world, and as a result of their interpretations our understanding of the relationship between man and nature has changed considerably, particularly during the last four hundred years. What was, in the sixteenth century, a definite faith in the observable, material world has now become a rather vague realisation that man is a part of the thing he observes, and as such is unable to see the world through the objective eyes of a true bystander. The conclusions of current philosophy, in particular the ideas of phenomenology, have seen to it that we can no longer differentiate between observed and experienced reality—what we dream and what we feel are now as real as the hard rock beneath our feet. Even modern science, with its reputation for objective and factual recording, reveals that matter and the universe as a whole become more mysterious and intangible with every discovery made. This general uncertainty and ambiguity is one of the most influential factors in determining the course of contemporary thought, and serious workers in every medium have been striving to come to terms with their own particular vision of reality. One would expect that photography, being so directly related to 'observed reality', would have a major part to play in this ferment of activity, and yet the possibilities inherent in the medium have been sadly neglected, except by a small percentage of determined workers. An examination of the work produced by these photographers does however reveal certain characteristics which are common to other media, and it is precisely these important characteristics which concern us here.

The Outlook of the Photographer

Ansel Adams, referring to some of his major works, has said: 'Sometimes I do believe I get to places just as something wonderful is about to happen', and this statement reveals the crucial aspect of his outlook. When he speaks of 'something wonderful', Adams clearly means an event which affects him deeply and which extends his understanding of the natural world, even if subconsciously. Perhaps he has been enraptured by the moon lighting the snowfields of Mount McKinley, or by the sight of clouds swirling amongst the sunlit cliffs of Yosemite—or else, perhaps simply by the sun setting from behind a heavy layer of cloud with the vast expanse of the Pacific below. In every case it is evident that his vision encompasses a faith in ultimate *order,* and that each photograph functions as an isolated expression of that order. Adams is of course only one of many such workers, and this faith in ultimate order is a recurrent feature of work in every medium.

As the meaning of order in this context is of the utmost importance it is imperative that it is not misunderstood, and as this article will be seen by many who are not directly concerned with this sphere of photography a little elaboration will perhaps not be amiss. It is probable that someone who has not previously encountered the concept will interpret it in terms of his own metaphysical frame of reference—to the Christian reader the order could be identified as the Deity, whereas the materialistic physicist could envisage it in terms of chance and probabilities. Such specific interpretations are not the intention here, and to understand the concept in its proper sense one has to adopt a strictly phenomenological approach; this means that one must 'forget' everything previously known and, as it were, start again, regarding as valid only that which is directly experienced. This outlook does in fact have very respectable antecedents including Einstein, who, when asked what proof he had that there existed a unity in nature, replied 'It is an act of faith'. Applied to the photographer of nature, this means that when he is confronted by 'something wonderful' he must react towards it in an entirely intuitive way, without regard for geography or physics—the response must come directly from the depths of his being. Of course, there is no such thing as an absolutely virgin experience which is unaffected by the various influences which may have acted upon the photographer from time to time, but these influences will tend to 'colour' the response rather than affect its basic essence. This distinction is, incidentally, the ultimate criterion of contemporaneity.

In achieving this method of working, the photographer is relying upon his knowledge of the craft of the medium to such an extent that he can produce, in one spontaneous act, what Raymond Moore has called 'the enlightened snapshot'. In so doing, the photographer is really collecting together the fragments of one complete work—each experience, suitably contained within the possibilities of the medium, is a single part of his vision of life. Each picture is, if you like, a visual 'clue' to the nature of the universe as it is envisaged by the photographer. The photography of nature is in itself

Text continued on page 152

ANSEL ADAMS

BILL BRANDT

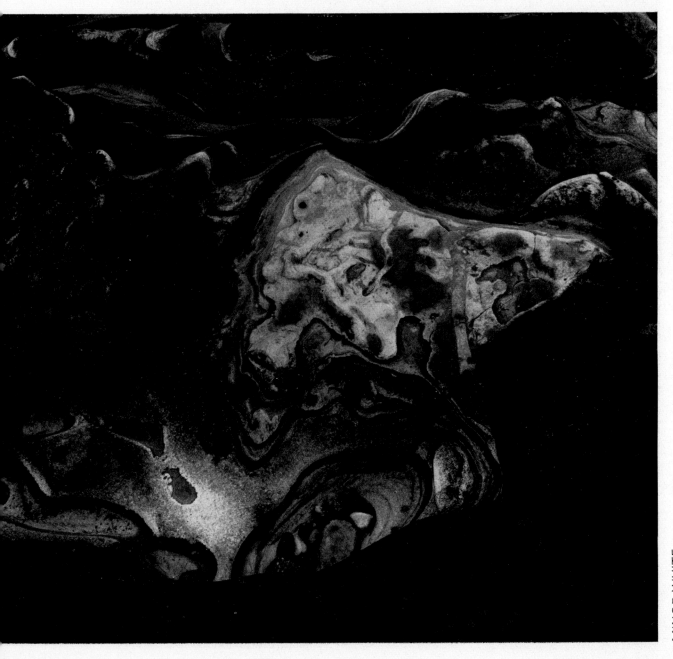

ANTHONY GRAHAM

RAYMOND MOORE

Text continued from page 145

a vast subject, and the sphere of interest occupied by a particular photographer is largely governed by temperament. Some photographers are concerned only with the vastness of nature—immense deserts, huge mountains, anything which typifies the massive boundlessness of nature occupies their attention. At the other extreme there are those photographers who find significance in the minutiae of nature—the sculptural qualities of rock, forms in the sand, and so on. In addition to these two extremes—and all that falls between them—there is another aspect which has held considerable fascination for many workers—the effects of nature upon the man-made. In this category of photography the camera is used to record the significant features of nature acting within the urban boundaries—moss grows on damp old walls, producing subtle metamorphoses; wind and rain transform posters into strange images of chance; nature somehow transforms everything that man makes until it eventually appears as 'natural' as the rest of the landscape.

Communication and Form

Having briefly surveyed the kinds of relationships which exist between the photographer and nature, we are left with the question of method. This question in turn poses many others, one of the most important of which is the concept of communication. Communication with another human being is seldom completely achieved and the idea is a fallacy. What invariably happens is that a worker uses his particular medium to channel the responses of an observer in a particular direction, after which the observer is entirely on his own, and whatever he finds in a particular work is ultimately a part of himself. This is not to say that when we look at a work by Minor White, for example, we do not share with him a delight in the sensuous forms of naturally eroded rock—indeed we do, and we may even see quite a lot of what he has seen. But finally, when we arrive at the absolute core of the visual experience, it is unlikely that our response will equal his, or anyone else's. It could be objected that such an approach would produce pictures which are subjective and hence private, but there are certain archetypal or basic forms to which we can all react—almost everyone is moved by a blazing sunset, for example—and it is the task of the photographer to select those images which are most likely to evoke responses from his audience. The onus of interpretation does not lie solely with the photographer however, since some audience contribution is essential if the work is to have lasting fascination, and naturally, some work requires considerable attention before its better qualities are revealed to us. However, before we can get anything from a photograph it is obvious that it must have *form*. The form of a photograph is responsible for the direction in which the previously mentioned channelling occurs, and hence finally, for its significance. The concept of form is an abstract and difficult one, and many interpretations and definitions have been put forward for it. The best and most comprehensive definition seen by this writer is that of Henry Holmes-Smith, who, deliberately paraphrasing Kenneth Burke's definition of literary form, said: 'Form in photography is the discovery and anticipation of an image. A photograph has form in so far as it

leads a viewer to anticipate and then to discover an image that corresponds in kind, quality and intensity with the one anticipated'. Expressed differently, this means that a photograph which has form provides us with a guide to the type of work which is its substance. We should be able to tell at a glance whether the work is record, reportage, evocative, or whatever—but most important is that this original impression should be reinforced and enriched by further and deeper contemplation of the work. The degree to which this relationship exists is a measure of the degree to which the photograph has form.

Returning the concepts of form and communication to the general heading of method, it will be seen that the photographer of nature does not set out to achieve absolute communication of what he has seen and felt—rather, by means of form, he directs our responses towards a realisation of *our own* basic feelings concerning his experiences in particular, and concerning the universe in general. An understanding of this important fact is without any doubt the key to understanding the nature of modern photography as a whole.

Summary

The analytical photographer sees the natural world through the eyes of a participating observer, and the results of his observations are therefore inherently concerned with man—what he thinks, what he feels, what he senses. Above all, he is concerned with describing the reality which he has experienced for himself, rather than with observations which stem from the accepted standards of reality to which we once clung. The cow in the lush meadow or the swan floating gracefully on the river would be impertinent irrelevances today. Significant photography today is concerned with resolving the disparity between instinct and understanding in an age which is dominated by the machine and our sense of natural beauty is diminished by the synthetic nature of our urban environment. In 'Fratricide', Franz Kafka wrote:

"The night sky called to him enticingly; he was drawn to the dark blue and the gold. Knowing nothing, he gazes up at it; in ignorance, he smoothes the hair beneath the hat that he has raised; the masses above do not group closer together to clear the view of his immediate future; everything remains immobile, senseless, unfathomable . . ."

This picture of an alienated being pertinently describes our condition regarding the natural world today. Sometimes however, there are photographers who allow us a glimpse . . .

Note on the Illustrations

The accompanying photographs are taken from sources as wide apart as possible and represent a cross-section of attitudes which have appeared during the period from 1940 to the present day.

After careful consideration it was decided that the photographs should be left to the imagination and patience of the viewer, and not described or 'explained' in any way. Since some of them are a little difficult to take in without repeated viewing, one can only advise persistence. Persistence does pay however, and perseverance in the face of any difficulty which may be met will result in enrichment of one's visual experience.

EPITOME OF PROGRESS

The Specialist Contributors of The British Journal of Photography survey the past year

EDUCATION

Any comment on the progress of photographic education must be seen in the larger context of the developments over the past year which have influenced large segments of the entire further education sector.

Firstly, many of the proposed polytechnics have become a reality. The concept for these was first put forward in a government White Paper 'A Plan for Polytechnics and Other Colleges' in 1966. Several large schools of photography have found themselves within the Art and Design faculties of these large educational complexes. The opportunity of being able to call upon specialists in technology and commerce to help implement full-time courses, as well as offering basic and specialist courses in photography throughout the polytechnic, is an exciting prospect. In actual fact, the problems of bringing together a combined administration and new academic boards are producing their own teething troubles. Whatever the immediate disadvantages, hopefully, these will be outweighed by the obvious long-term advantages.

Secondly, the joint report by the National Advisory Council on Art Education and the National Council for Diplomas in Art and Design 'The Structure of Art and Design Education' has brought upheaval in the Art and Design field. The hopes of incorporating photography into the current DipAD Graphic Design courses would appear to have diminished. The report says (quote), 'We would not wish at this time to comment on arrangements for courses of specialised vocational or professional study normally recruiting students aged 18 or over which are associated with the awards of professional bodies and approved by the Department of Education and Science.' A footnote to this statement specifically cites the examinations of the Institute of Incorporated Photographers as falling within this category. The general body of the report has two major recommendations of interest to photography; firstly, modification of current DipAD courses to permit greater flexibility, and secondly, a two-tier structure of DipAD. 'Group A' courses will be provided by the continued operation of courses similar to those currently offered; 'Group B' courses will be directed more specifically towards certain categories of industrial and professional design practice. Educationalists may see 'Group B' courses as a way of incorporating photography as a major study into DipAD.

The 'Notice of Intent' published by the Institute of Incorporated Photographers in 1966 has taken effect on a national scale over the past year. The last IIP Intermediate examination was held in 1970 and the last Final examination is scheduled for 1972. The Professional Qualifying Examination is now the first level course. This is an Institute-recognised and assessed three-year full-time (or the equivalent sandwich or part-time) course. For recognition the individual college submits its proposed course to the Institute. This freedom within the limits prescribed by the Institute allows for a flexibility which is desirable in a profession as diversified as photography. Minimum entry requirements are GCE 'O' level passes in English Language and four other appropriate subjects, including at least one 'A' level (or equivalent qualifications). Minimum age of entry is 18 years. During the past year courses at Birmingham Polytechnic and the London College of Printing have been recognised. Previous to this the only recognised courses were at Harrow College of Technology and the Manchester Polytechnic.

The IIP second level course is the Vocational Course in Photography. Recognition by the Institution is made on the school's individual application which is based on the Institute's national syllabuses. This is intended to enable schools to meet both the basic requirements of the Institute along with regional demands or specialisations. The minimum entry requirements are GCE 'O' level passes in English Language and three other appropriate subjects. Minimum age of entry is 16 years. First courses under this scheme were recognised as of September 1968 and now include Blackpool, Edinburgh (Napier), Glasgow, Gloucester, Leeds (Kitson), and Plymouth. In addition a three-year part-time course is run by Twickenham. The first examination was held in the summer of 1970. This scheme will run without major modifications until at least 1973.

The Institute itself is in the process of restructuring many aspects of its activities. Graduates with the Professional Qualifying Examination Certificate with two years' appropriate professional experience are awarded the Associateship of the Institute; while holders of the Vocational Examination in Photography Certificate with two years' professional experience and having attained the age of 23 are awarded the Licentiateship. This now gives a clearly defined path of qualification development.

The Polytechnic of Central London has recently become the first establishment in the country to offer a BA degree in Photographic Arts approved by the Council for National Academic Awards. This is in addition to their BSc Honours degree in Photographic Technology. It is interesting to see from the current CNAA Annual Report that there are several individuals in the country registered as working for 'higher' degrees in both photography and photographic technology. Refreshingly, through all this rush to be 'recognised' the Royal College of Art continues to run its two-year DipRCA course independent of anybody.

While the Institute tends to cater predominantly for full-time students the City and Guilds of London Institute continues its policy of part-time courses involving day release, block release and evening study. There are two basic schemes; 344 General Photography Certificate and 345 Photographic Technician's Certificate. While the student will be working in the appropriate area of photography there are no minimum educational requirements for admission to these courses or examinations, but it is expected that he or she will have acquired a knowledge of English, Science and Mathematics equivalent to that provided in the fifth year CSE course at a secondary school. While this will not be examined, the student will be required to take a course in General Studies, including English, to enable him to acquire some measure of skill in communication, and in particular the ability to absorb and interpret information.

The part-time courses for the General Photography Certificate covers a period of three years. This may be followed by the General Photography Advanced Certificate which occupies a further two years' part-time study. The basic scheme is intended to meet the requirements of students who are employed as photographers, printers or studio assistants in the fields of portraiture, commercial, advertising and fashion photography. The Advanced Scheme aims to increase the student's depth of photographic knowledge and prepare him for a considerable degree of personal responsibility, both in the organisation, planning and execution of his work as a photographer and in the supervision of others. The 345 Photographic Technician's Certificate is intended to meet the requirements of students who are already employed as photographic technicians in research, industry and allied fields or in the photofinishing industry and commercial colour laboratories. The three-year technician's course has been designed to enable students to specialise in their third year. The first and second years are common to both groups. Advanced study in greater depth and specialisation allows the student to take either the Photographic Technician's Advanced Certificate Course, or commencing in September 1971, the Photographic Colour Laboratory Technician's Advanced Certificate Course.

A new contender into the field of photographic qualifications is the Society of Industrial Artists and Designers. Under the umbrella of Panel D (Graphics) they have instigated a new category in 'Creative Photography'. For the purposes of entry into this category, Creative Photography is defined as 'the production of photography or photographic designs for visual communications media where visual perception, expression and communications are paramount'. Candidates will be expected to submit six published assignments, with commissioning details, six additional pictures and one case history. Successful candidates will receive the designatory letters of MSIA and FSIA.

At the time of writing the decision on Britain's entry into the Common Market is unknown. The Europhot 'First International Symposium on Vocational Education' held in Brussels in November 1969 made several recommendations to its general assembly which if acted upon will influence the future pattern of British photographic education. These were:

1 A Europhot teacher qualification, teacher seminars and teacher exchanges.
2 A Europhot recognition of European schools of photography for specified subjects and levels.
3 Europhot rationalisation of photographic education facilities.
4 Europhot schools of photography International student exchanges.
5 A Europhot professional qualification that is internationally valid for legal purposes and employment evaluation.

These proposals, which did not always carry the support of the British delegation, obviously have far-reaching consequences and are open to a range of interpretation. The major factor is that in principle they are in existence and perhaps are an indication of one channel of development.

While the work of the Industrial Training Boards may not be considered by some as 'education', they are fulfilling their objective of improving the quality of industrial training.

The 'taking and selling of photographs' comes within the scope of the Printing and Publishing Industrial Training Board while some photographic establishments which are process houses come within the scope of the Chemical Industry Training Board. Equally important, educationally and socially, was 'Professional Photography 1971'. This was the first international convention organised by the IIP and held in Brighton during March 1971. While completely different in their conception, both the ITB's and the convention are examples of 'retraining'. With the increasing speed of technological and social change, retraining of long-established photographers and management is becoming a necessity of our society.

The most important change in photographic education is in the course content and academic attitudes towards photography. Photography has for a long time acted as a service to other schools, but appeared reticent to be anything but insular within its own self. This gale force wind of change is opening many doors, and photography courses are becoming truly interdisciplinary, as they need to be if the quality of photographic education is to rise to meet the needs of industry in the future.

MICHAEL HALLETT

AUDIO-VISUAL AIDS

It is not so much that the audio-visual equipment field has gone stagnant, as that the number of slips 'twixt cup and lip seem to be increasing. EVR will have taken three years between its first demonstration and its first use in a practical training situation. The Philips PIP equipment has been two years getting onto the market, as have the Sony and the Philips ½in cassette VTR. Even the Singer/Graflex Instaload 16mm projector took a year before orders could be supplied. Maybe it is just that the publicity boys are quicker off the mark than their production colleagues, though one

suspects—more darkly—that the early announcement practice is intended to damage sales of existing products as well as simply to create interest in the one being promoted. This is, perhaps, even understandable in a market where money is anything but plentiful, and sales of new types of hardware can usually be obtained only at the expense of budgets for existing types.

Right now, indeed, one might be excused for hoping that the wave of invention would halt, so that the manufacturers could settle down to producing and refining some equipments which can really be put to work; and, even more important, so that the producers of the learning materials, without which all the equipment in the world is useless, can get ahead with making software with some certainty that it will suit the system for which it is designed. Production of programmes which really exploit the facilities of the new equipments is an expensive business because it must be done from scratch. One of the worst features of the EVR presentation is that it is all being based on 16mm film transferred to the new medium—which simply gives you poor quality, small-image 16mm film! Materials for the new PIP (Programmed Individual Presentation) equipment, for example, need to be tightly programmed to make use of the instant progression from still pictures to movie sequences at any speed up to 24fps, linked to synchronised sound: programmes of this nature, which break out of the restrictions imposed by ordinary film or ordinary still projection systems, require far more thought, far more understanding of the ways in which people learn, far more sheer creativity than presentation on any single medium system—and that means more initial expense in creating the programmes. The pay-off, of course, comes in far more effective learning as a result of all the effort.

The PIP system, and the similar, though incompatible, American RCS Module system, is simple in concept—although apparently very difficult to achieve mechanically. It is a development from the synchronised sound/filmstrip or tape/slide presentations we have known for years. The image, in this case, is carried on Super 8 film, whilst the sound and the synchronising pulses are carried on a separate audio tape. In the PIP equipment two cassettes are used—one for film, the other a standard compact cassette for sound. The RCS system houses both film and sound tape in the one plastic cassette. The synchronising pulses in both systems are arranged so that it is possible to advance the film frame by frame slowly, as in 35mm sound filmstrips, or up to a speed of 24 frames a second. This means that stills, semi-animation, or full cine film can all be programmed together on one machine. This, allied to the fact that both machines are integral rear-projection units, makes them potentially valuable additions to teaching hardware.

It is virtually certain that the high cost of making sophisticated programmes for complicated equipments is one of the major reasons for the relatively much greater rate of adoption of those equipments which use 'do-it-yourself' teaching materials. The best example of this is the overhead projector, which is almost at the stage of being ordered as a matter of course by everyone who believes in a visual approach to learning. Every teacher and training officer feels that he can cope with the production of transparencies suited directly to the way *he* teaches *his* subject: whilst, frankly, this is not true—the standard of production of some transparencies one sees is abysmal, both in concept and in execution—it is certainly creating a rapidly expanding market for acetate sheet, spirit pens and wax pencils and all the other do-it-yourself paraphernalia of overhead projection. The equipment has settled into an accepted pattern and standard of performance, and we are now experiencing a period of refinement as a means of competition. Several equipments offer automatic lamp-changing, eliminating delays caused by the difficulty of handling the high-temperature tungsten-halogen lamps immediately after failure, and Bell & Howell's latest model has a mirror incorporated in the head assembly which permits the projection of the picture in four directions—which should satisfy the demands of any conceivable teaching situation! This year has seen, too, the marketing of the first fully integrated system of materials for the production, use and storage of overhead projector transparencies. The 'Integer' system, as it is known, has been very carefully thought out: the use of accurately punched acetate sheets and card mounts in conjunction with a register board for both preparation of the transparencies and use during projection means that full registration between overlays in a set can be maintained at all times. Provision is also made for storage of unmounted sheets and for a visual five digit decimal indexing system to aid filing and retrieval.

Many teachers, of course, are competent amateur photographers and the ease with which acceptable 35mm colour slides can be made is no doubt a major contributory factor in the increasing popularity of synchronised tape-slide presentations. There have been at least three new cassette tape-recorders specially modified for the production of synch pulse tapes; a version of the Philips stereo recorder, the Transensor equipment which is added to a Philips N2202, and the Jonan distributed by Hanimex. These are used in conjunction with a wide range of projection equipment, amongst which the Kodak Carousel still holds the lead position, but is finding competition from the Hanimex Rondex. If only the 8mm warfare could be terminated, this field too would almost certainly respond to the current do-it-yourself trend. Education has almost accepted the death of Standard 8 except for use in published cassette-loop films, but the format problem is now superseded by the cartridge war. Whether to go for the Kodak cartridge, used on the admirable Eumig 711R, or the Bell & Howell cartridge which fits their Model 459 Auto 8 projector, is the sort of decision the educator wants to avoid. He normally does it by using neither—sacrificing ease of operation whilst he waits for someone else to force a decision. This is a great pity, for the 8mm gauge will only make its full impact in education when a standard as firm as that for 16mm is established.

Technical advance and a growing market has led to video-tape recorders becoming both easier to use and markedly cheaper. This is an equipment which could well become as common in schools as audio-tape recorders were a few years ago. Their main use will be as a means of 'fixing' television broadcasts so that they can be fitted into more convenient parts of the daily timetable: but again their use with cheaper CCTV cameras could lead to some 'in-school' production of teaching material. We have been promised a simple cassette-VTR machine for two years now, and as this article is written there is still a chance that either the Philips or the Sony equipments—using miracle of miracles, the same standard cassette—will reach the market before the end of 1971. It remains to be seen whether performance from these equipments is as good as the prototype demonstrations are rumoured to have been, but if they are, there could well be a dramatic increase in the use of video-tape recorders in 1972-3.

Whether or not an increased use of VTRs will affect the number of 16mm projectors in use is open to question—but it seems to me unlikely. Television is essentially a small-group medium, and remains a relatively low picture-quality medium, especially so far as colour is concerned. But certainly new projectors like the Singer/Graflex Instaload could do much to keep up the level of use of 16mm film. Not only is it good from the point of view of mechanics and light output it is also quiet and dramatically easy to use. Its lacing path is similar to a tape-recorder: just drop the film into the slot, push the button and show! Indeed controls and operation are like a tape-recorder—fast forward and rewind are allied to easy loading. And there is the added advantage that in its basic form the price is very competitive with existing 16mm projectors.

Before ending this review of the audio-visual field in 1971 mention must be made of the growing use of various types of equipment for individual tuition in primary schools. A few years ago the thought of giving a six-year-old child his own tape-recorder to operate would have induced instant apoplexy in the majority of head-teachers and local authority advisers. Now it is almost a commonplace—and certainly a most inspiring experience—to see an infant school child chatting happily and productively, into the microphone of a Language Master, or a little cassette recorder; or gazing at slides on a hand-viewer and listening to a story through headphones as a teacher tells a story to him alone—while she copes at the same time with 29 other individuals. Synchrofax machines; the Rank Talking Page; Polaroid Cameras; individual filmstrip and slide viewers; all of these are being safely and productively handled by infant age children—whilst the 'grown-ups' of nine and ten in primary school are making 8mm films and 35mm slides which many adults would be proud of. A class of top-year infants (about seven years old) watched a student teacher trying to load the school tape-recorder patiently some moments before one of them said gently 'would you let me do that—I am the regular operator!' There is a sign of the times.

N. E. WILLIS

REPROGRAPHY

Printing began as a craft which relied for many generations on know-how and the experience of men who had learned *how* to do things without, in many instances, knowing precisely *why*. There are many engaged in the industry today who recollect that methods and techniques depended upon what was almost folklore passed jealously down from father to son within the narrow limits of 'the family business'. This has changed, the family business is being replaced by the combine and the consortium and it is now accepted that organised knowledge, measurement and system can do better than mysterious 'green fingers'. The battle waged by the technologist in print has been long and protracted, but it is a battle that has been won. Change challenges human institutions and the human beings that build them. Some changes are so potent that men and their institutions must quickly adapt or perish. The pages of history are littered with the wreckage of inflexible institutions that technology has challenged and eventually changed or superseded—the craft guild made obsolete by the factory system, the general practitioner giving way to the specialist—and in the graphic processes the technician, technologist and management consultant replacing the purely craft approach.

The vexed question of ink-water balance has always presented a problem in lithographic printing. Over the years much research and development has been initiated and pursued and the ideal of being able to print from planographic plates without water ever seemed elusive of realisation. The breakthrough has now occurred. Ronald Trist, a chemist and engineer in the late 1920s, introduced the Pantone Process which was a dry litho method. Unfortunately the process employed a mercury amalgam which, because of its toxicity and the fact that it constituted a health hazard, caused the process to be abandoned and discontinued. Now the Minnesota Mining and Manufacturing Company (3M) have marketed a system of dry lithography named Driography which is based upon the research, over a number of years, of John F. Curtin, a 3M physicist. The method uses a silicon rubber with a very low release-value coated on a diazo sensitised aluminium surface. Exposure to a negative makes the diazo sensitiser soluble in an organic developer and the final printing plate consists of metal in the image areas and silicon rubber in the non-image areas. The absence of water simplifies operations and procedure to a remarkable degree. There is no ink-water balance, fountain solution, pH, gum and alcohol concentration, buffering faction, ink emulsification, coating, piling, tinting, etc, to worry about. The elimination of the dampening system on the press in itself represents a significant saving with faster start-ups an restarts giving increased production per hour with less paper waste. Paper manufacturers welcome this development as the elimination of water minimises paper stretch and a dimensionally stable sheet eliminates many problems such as paper cure, picking and, of course, misregister. Without the water involvement, ink drying will be faster and the inks have a higher tack which means better quality and density of impression. Obviously there are problems to solve, particularly in relation to the ink used for printing. 3M have modified ordinary lithographic inks, increasing the cohesive forces to eliminate any tendency for the inks to wet the non-printing areas of the plates which have a low surface energy. This causes the inks to print sharper, but they have a tendency to pile on the rollers and blankets and do not absorb into the paper as rapidly as conventional inks. Problems of marking or tracking on web presses have to be solved and the increased cohesive forces of the inks tend, at present, to dusting and linting on the plates—probably on account of the fact that the blanket is dry. Thus considerable work remains to be done in formulating the optimum inks for the Driographic process and the characteristics of the special inks will determine whether modifications in paper requirement will be necessary. More field testing with new ink formulations on uncoated and coated papers continues apace using the new plates.

Other plate manufacturers are working along similar lines—for example H.F. Gipe of Baltimore has also patented a waterless lithographic system in which the printing areas of the plate consist of metal and the non-printing areas consist of a silicon rubber. Along more orthodox lines the Teeg Plate marketed by the Durolith Corporation of Detroit is a positive working plate which apparently has an inorganic lithographic surface which, after exposure, provides the water carrying and ink receptive areas without development, so that the plate is simply wetted and inked to prepare for printing. Its remarkable degree of hardness means that it can compete successfully in the present highly competitive multi-metal market. The manufacturers use the term 'photohydrophilicity' to express the creation of water receptivity with light. Before exposure the surface is hydrophobic and completely unaffected by water vapour and oxygen.

It is interesting to recall that during the past twelve months important steps have been made in the development of solventless inks which are exempt from air pollution regulations. One ink system has been designed primarily for web printing and uses cross-linking pre-polymers with heat sensitive catalysts and a conventional web dryer. These inks are at present more costly than conventional inks and require a paper temperature as high as 150°C which tends to blistering. A further formulation, which can be used for sheet fed or web fed work, uses liquid photo-polymers which solidify on exposure to large amounts of ultra-violet radiations. These inks are also at present expensive and the u.v. equipment is costly as it requires extensive cooling facilities to avoid undue heating of the press and paper plus complete shielding to prevent eye damage.

Progress in electronic scanning has been steady rather than spectacular during the past months, the exception being the announcement that a new colour scanner has been developed by Ventures Research & Development Group that uses a digital computer which can be automatically programmed for any printing system, and which can enlarge, reduce, merge copy and be operated by remote control. The programme is determined by scanning a special colour chart which consists of 512 colour blocks printed on the press with the paper and inks to be used in printing. It produces screened separations directly and has provision for saturation control to bring the range of colours on the original copy within the range of the printing inks. The equipment includes semi-automatic colour balance and retouching control to eliminate the need for dot etching the separations for local corrections. The digital scanner with its capacity to store information makes it possible to transmit data concerning copy, size, etc, to remote locations. Digitising techniques to record and store temporarily the results of scanning are featured in all modern scanners including the Crosfield Magnascan 450 and the Dr Hell Chromograph DC 300. This obviously could help development in two directions, transmission of colour pictures and the combination of (digitised) text and picture information to form complete text pages in future typesetting compositing operations. It is also feasible that the present use of vignetted contact screens for half-tone dot scanning will eventually be replaced by digitised methods of creating the screen pattern and dot formation. The latest and by far the fastest of the Chromograph range of scanners (DC 300) combines screening, enlarging, colour separating in one operation under daylight conditions, using an automatic system of film loading in light-tight cassettes. Three interchangeable scanning drums are available and an A4 page can be scanned in $2\frac{1}{2}$ minutes. Direct screening, 3×1 reduction up to 1×16 enlargement is accommodated with the facility for combination work and lateral and negative to positive reversal. Each of the four colour channels has ten separate controls for versatility in adjusting colour correction and tonal values with special controls for the equalisation or alteration of colour casts throughout the tonal range and a multi-point switch preselects the required grey balance and gradation for the selected printing process.

Forty-eight fully colour corrected separations in less than 4 minutes scanning time are possible with the current version of the Linotype-Paul Linoscan 204 colour scanner. Twelve 6×6cm transparencies can be mounted in two rows of six, and the traversing speed of the Linoscan is 40mm per minute at a resolution of 200 lines per cm. The scanning carriage therefore traverses 15cm in $3\frac{3}{4}$ minutes, during which time all four colour-corrected separations are exposed simultaneously on two sheets of film. If an allowance of 15 minutes is made for setting up and 11 minutes for automatic processing the total production time for the 12 complete colour sets amounts to 30 minutes, which is equivalent to $2\frac{1}{2}$ minutes per four colours. By similar utilisation of the drum format, $10 \times 12 \cdot 5$cm transparencies can be grouped four up to expose 16 colour separations in $3\frac{3}{4}$ minutes scanning time at 200 lines per cm. Inclusive of setting-up time and processing the total production time for finished film negatives or positives is equivalent to $7\frac{1}{2}$ minutes per colour set, less than 2 minutes per colour separation. The equipment will scan and expose any area up to the maximum format of 30×40cm, two colours at a time, and will also expose all four colours simultaneously within the format of 15×40cm.

In Europe and America there are now well over 1000 computers being used for typesetting. In 5 years the number of firms using computers has increased more than fourteenfold, and the gain on last year is 33% in the number of computer composing installations. Phototypesetting is expected to mushroom 300% in the next 5 years to become, according to American statistics, a £50,000,000pa business. Medium priced electronic CRT devices and low-priced text-orientated machines can be expected to be marketed and sold in considerable numbers, but the extremely fast, high-priced CRT machines will, in all probability, reach market saturation before this time on account of their high output and capability. It is a fact that eight CRT machines, working a single shift, could typeset all the books published annually in the United States.

The first European RCA Videocomp 70/800 computerised typesetting system has been installed by Computaprint Limited, the bureau division of IPC Business Press. It offers exceptional capacity, high operating speed and virtually unlimited flexibility in the range of typefaces it can handle. Fully composed pages for directories, dictionaries, encyclopaedias, etc, are set in type sizes from 4 to 96pt in lines as long as 70ems (11·67in) on to stabilisation paper, paper plates or film with setting speeds of up to 6000 characters per second. Many styles and sizes of type founts are available and each character can be altered electronically to provide an unlimited mix of characters. Text to be typeset is generated in the required line and character sequence by phototypesetting programmes, run on an IBM computer and written for each individual job using powerful RCA and Computaprint software. The equipment performs on either magnetic tape or disc and all forms of line work can be freely interspersed with the text. It can produce, for example, line drawings in a few seconds at a resolution of 450 strokes per inch and can digitise and store drawings from 35mm transparencies for subsequent reproduction. The microfilming capacity is first-rate in that besides producing complete full-size pages of film ready for plate-making, it can produce high-quality text and line drawings directly on to 35mm microfilm for easy storage and retrieval.

Phototypsetting developments have stimulated interest in plastic plate production for letterpress printing and also initiated improved machine control and faster etching times in powderless etching. One of West Germany's largest chemical companies, Hoechst of Dusseldorf, has patented an etchable plastic printing plate. Image areas on the polyoxymethyl-plate are blocked with an acid-resistant varnish after which the varnish-free areas are etched with sulphuric or other mineral acid. Advantages claimed are outstanding surface hardness and scratch resistance, low abrasion and high dimensional stability. Long-run testing to date has produced no noticeable wear in the sharpness of the printed image.

Several new proofing processes are now available for pre-press colour proofing. One which claims to be able to match ink shades used in press runs has been developed by Staley Graphics & The Batelle Memorial Institute of Columbus, Ohio. The process (Colex) uses a light sensitive coating in combination with dry developing powders and a special proofing paper. The method uses a light-induced physical change in the surface layer of the proofing material which alters its deformation characteristics so that the powders are selectively embedded into, or rejected by, the light altered surface. Both continuous tone and screened half-tones can be reproduced in black-or-white or colour, as negatives or positives. Multi-colours are overprinted and exposure takes some 60 seconds per colour, the complete procedure being 5 to 6 minutes for colour proofs up to 25×38in.

Agfa-Gevaert have introduced Gevaproof, Du Pont—Cromalin and Kodak a system referred to as photothermographic proofing. All these new systems produce proofs on an integral base and require special equipment. The 1826 Electrostatic Proofing System is marketed by the S.D. Warren Graphic Arts Product Group. It is very suitable for type-matter proofing and uses a liquid toner, producing an 18×26in proof in less than 40 seconds. This Company is also in the final stages of developing another proofing machine, called the Fotofinisher 842, for dry proofing.

ERIC CHAMBERS

MEDICAL

Progress in Medical illustration is governed by many developments outside the profession, for example, progress in optical design and fibre optics enables better results to be obtained in endoscopy. Better results mean easier interpretation and a more accurate diagnosis. Thus, an improvement in a hospital can benefit every service that is provided to diagnose, treat and comfort a patient. During the past year many hospital building programmes have been started or are in the course of completion, some of these schemes which are multi-million pound projects and have made news in the national press, have incorporated educational centres. These centres have been established with the idea of centralising educational activity, that is, the postgraduate, general practitioner, nurse training and paramedical training under one roof. These various training programmes can benefit from improved teaching and library services and can also share the facilities of an illustration unit which provides the soft ware. New departments of medical photography mean better working facilities and equipment and in turn a better end product. Nearly every region in the country has some improvement, a new photographic department was included in the new Southend General Hospital development in Essex. The new multi-million pound development of the Norwich hospitals which serve East Anglia has a large new department included in its first phase. A generous donation of £20,000 from the USA enabled the Plastic Surgery and Burns Unit at the Queen Victoria Hospital, East Grinstead to build a new photographic unit. In South Wales a £20,000,000 hospital complex near Cardiff is nearing completion and this has an illustration unit embracing about 3000sq ft. Southampton was selected as the site for a new medical school. The new school has a large academic teaching block which houses a new illustration unit, which will embrace a processing laboratory area of 3000sq ft, a studio area of 1500sq ft and an offset printing unit of 500sq ft. Also in Southampton a new Regional photographic Unit was opened to serve the Wessex Region. New plans are also being made for the development of regional services in Birmingham. North of the border there are other numerous developments, particularly in the Glasgow area.

The development of educational technology in medicine is a parallel development with new educational centres in the new teaching complexes. The development of hardware and software and assessment of the value of the equipment in teaching and the long-term results are now becoming available. The emphasis on the tape slide lectures has been more noticeable in recent years and in 1970 there were three conferences where the results of tape slide teaching methods and the use of AVA were discussed. The IMBI annual conference at Newcastle-upon-Tyne covered many aspects of medical illustration. A conference on the audio-visual resources in medical education was held in Glasgow later in the year. This conference concentrated more on the audio-visual aspect and covered in depth the methods of planning and making tape slide lectures, programmed learning and teaching programmes, open and closed circuit television and methods of presentation. Another conference on tape slide teaching, a one-day meeting was organised by the Medical Recording Service Foundation, and the subjects discussed varied from pathology to veterinary teaching. Thus during the past year there has been a definite increase in the use of AVA in the biological and life sciences, but we must remember the comment Sir Brynmor Jones made in his opening address to the Glasgow conference ... AVA are a fundamental approach to teaching and a response does not guarantee understanding ...

Another development has been the commercial interest in post-graduate education for the general practitioner. Two companies have produced educational programmes with similar aims, the involvement of the audience. The first company is Medicovision, which is sponsored by Roche Products Limited. The idea behind Medicovision is a project involving Switzerland, France, Germany and Great Britain to produce one-inch video tape recordings in colour. The tape programme is replayed through a recorder to 23-inch colour monitors, the number of monitors depending upon the size of the audience. The length of the programmes average about 30 minutes and are constructed so that they should be open-ended allowing them to lead on to active group discussion, the film recording is used to create a situation upon which discussion can be based.

The second firm is General Practitioner Studies, their method is to produce medical teaching programmes in the form of films which include planned audience participation. The films are in two parts, the first half presents the case histories and requires the audience to participate by writing answers to questions posed during the film. The second part represents the cases but gives in more detail the results of diagnostic investigations and also demonstrates alternative diagnosis.

What about photography and its applications to medicine, development of techniques for specific situations are usually the work of a team of people over a period of time. The most relevant advance is the work of C. P. Hodge of Montreal, Canada, who was awarded the 1970 RPS Combined Royal Colleges Award Medal for his work on flourescein angiography. He had used cine, still, Polaroid and VTR recordings to help to record the blood flow through vessels in the brain which enabled diseased areas to be demarcated at the time of operation. This technique is the result of nearly ten years' work.

Another technique for investigating the depth and area of burns and scalds is being developed at the plastic surgery centre, Queen Victoria Hospital, East Grinstead. The method being used is colour thermography and to help the development of this technique the centre was given a Kodak award of £500. Photogrammetry has also come back onto the scene, with the publication of a paper on stereophotogrammetic method to investigate facial changes following the loss of teeth. This again was a team effort embracing the department of Dental Prosthetics, University of Glasgow and departments of Surveying and Photography and the Teaching Aids laboratory University of Newcastle upon Tyne.

The development of sophisticated techniques plus the involvement in the production teaching programmes indicates the trend of medical illustration in the future and makes the medical photographer and artist a team member instead of isolationists that they have been in the past.

J. H. BURNARD

FINANCE AND TRADE

—US Companies

Eastman Kodak	Total Sales ($)	Net Income ($)
1970	27,846,000	40,366,000
1969	27,472,000	40,114,000
1968	26,441,000	37,537,000
1967	23,915,000	35,226,000
1966	21,493,000	35,667,000

Polaroid	Gross Revenue ($)	Net Income ($)
1970	44,429,000	6,114,000
1969	46,561,000	6,186,000
1968	40,207,000	5,890,000
1967	37,435,000	5,738,000
1966	31,555,000	4,759,000

Bell & Howell	Net Sales ($)	Net Income ($)
1970	29,776,000	1,096,000
1969	29,779,000	1,091,000
1968	28,055,000	1,251,000
1967	26,954,000	1,187,000
1966	25,623,000	934,000

GAF Corporation	Gross Sales ($)	Net Income ($)
1970	58,971,000	839,000
1969	60,525,000	1,524,000
1968	56,955,000	2,123,000
1967	52,087,000	1,896,000
1966	48,406,000	2,227,000

Pako Corpn	Net Sales ($)	Net Income ($)
1970	30,776,000	1,109,000
1969	30,529,000	1,793,000
1968	25,222,000	1,417,000
1967	23,679,000	1,898,000
1966	18,834,000	1,636,000

From the above table it will be seen that Sales and Income for Eastman Kodak have been steadily upwards for the past half decade: that Revenue and Income for Polaroid reacted slightly from the new high level of the previous year: that Bell & Howell's Sales were slightly down and its Income slightly up: that GAF Corporation's Sales and Income were both down: that Pako Corporation's Sales were up but Income down.

The latest figures for **Eastman Kodak** were accompanied by the advice, first, that over $171,000,000 had been spent on research and development programmes carried forward world-wide. These programmes continued to produce fundamentally new and improved films, papers and processing chemistry which promised to widen the scope and effectiveness with which Kodak products and services can be used. Fields explored were the provision of films for in-camera processing, the investigation of non-silver imaging materials, the design of personal microfilm viewers, the development of new copying and duplicating systems, efforts to devise economic ways of using TV sets for the display of both self-produced and programmed entertainment, the construction of new systems for recording computer output and the evolution of cameras that combine the best of optics, mechanics and electronics. The proportion of colour film sales to black-and-white was reported as having achieved another advance. Much of this increase was traceable to the Kodak Instamatic camera, the owners of which buy about ten rolls of colour film for each roll of black-and-white. More than half of the company's amateur film sales were size 126 for cartridge loading cameras.

The Kodak Instamatic 'X' camera was further noticed with the advice that a family of five new models, introduced in July, promised snapshooters a new era of success and reliability in flash-picture taking. These cameras used the new magicube which flashes on mechanical impact from a torsion spring. As they are free from reliance on a battery generated electrical impulse to energise the flash-lamp, the Instamatic 'X' cameras eliminate picture losses formerly caused by insufficient battery charge. All models feature systems which show a warning in the viewfinder whenever a used lamp is facing the subject. The Kodak Carousel projector was stated to have acquired a new 140-slide tray which increased the previous store-and-show capacity by 75%. This new tray would operate with most Carousel projectors and would also accept regular and thin plastic mounts.

Radiography was covered with the advice that sales of Kodak X-Ray films, chemicals and processing equipment continued on the upwards trajectory of recent years, that the demand for medical X-Ray film, which has been growing in the USA at an annual rate of nearly 10% for close on a decade, showed no diminishing trend.

A complete new family of rapid-process films had been introduced to meet the widely ranging diagnostic needs. These included a high speed film to stop the motion of living organs, a special film for mammography, a new dental X-Ray film which gives full-depth information on tooth and gum tissue where, formerly, both front and back exposures were required.

In the business systems field, sales of microfilm rose substantially. Demand for record-using equipment, however, declined slightly, as did demand for copy and duplicating products; but sensitised products for the reproduction of engineering drawings, in spite of lower equipment sales, moved up. Otherwise in this field, the new Kodak KOM-80 microfilmer for computer output is a variable speed unit which can be configured to operate at rates from 60,000 characters a second to 120,000 characters a second, the latter in phased-encoded applications only. Other new products included a reader-printer that delivered dry prints from either positive or negative microforms: two new microfilm readers: a daylight-loading microfilm processor which accepts new cartridges from computer-output microfilmers.

In the professional, commercial and industrial photographic fields, sales of films, plates and chemicals used for lithographic printing continued their strong advance. The demand for colour papers increased substantially in spite of marked declines in the sales of photo-finishing equipment. Sales of data recording film and organic chemical sales increased strongly but a lower trend was evident in photo-fabrication and aerial photography products sales.

The Kodak Polymatic litho plate processor, a recent introduction, was envisaged as causing a further demand for litho plates. Other new products included a processor for photo-typesetting, capable of a 50% greater output than existing models, and a new family of Kodalith films and chemicals designed for machine processing which provide quality equal or superior to results obtained manually: a new colour negative film, an automatic processor and new chemicals which offered the first practical method for handling long (up to 100 feet) film rolls increasingly popular for portraiture: all-liquid chemicals for black-and-white Versamat processors: a Royal X-Pan film with better resolution, optically brightened rapid-access papers with a greater range of weights and surfaces: an Ektalure paper with a warm-white basis for more pleasing black-and-white pictures. Aerial film sales were lower, but the Earth Resources Technology Satellite programme was envisaged as generating up to 100 million colour prints annually in the mammoth task of inventorying the earth's resources.

During 1970 $64,000,000 were spent, a record, to increase and improve the company's capacity for international service such as new building projects in practically every country in the Free World trading zone. During 1970, too, more than 6000 Kodak men and women participated in its creative effort.

The report for **Polaroid**, issued in conjunction with its figures for 1970, included the information that demand for colour film held up well but that camera sales were down. Margins were stated to have been restricted by heavy research costs as well as by engineering expenses on plants being built to manufacture the new generation of cameras and film under development.

The company's Colorpak II and Series 300 line of Polaroid Land cameras was stated to be manufactured for them by unaffiliated outside manufacturers pursuant to its design, plans and specification, and subject to quality supervision. Most Polaroid Land film was manufactured by the company itself, but certain components for the film were made by outside concerns. In this context it was advised that, under an agreement entered into with Eastman Kodak in December of 1969, Kodak would continue to supply them with colour negatives for PRD's Type 108 film, this being used for the present line of Polaroid cameras, for five years or more. The agreement also granted Kodak a royalty-bearing licence to make and market Polaroid Type 108 film beginning 1976, or possibly 1975. Research, engineering and manufacturing expenses

were about $58,000,000 compared with $40,600,000 in the previous year. These expenses were envisaged as remaining heavy, but some improvement in profit margins was anticipated as overhead costs were spread over a larger sales base.

New plant facilities were under construction in Massachusetts to provide for the manufacture of the new generation of cameras and film currently under development. Production 'bugs' on the colour negative for the new instant-colour film, being developed for the compact camera, could delay the introduction of the new portrait camera until after Eastman Kodak had come out with its own line of quick-developing photographic products. The portrait camera had a fixed focus and is to be priced at less than $20. Elsewhere, the new colourpack line of cameras had an improved flash and sharper focusing. It should, accordingly, produce better pictures, particularly indoors. A final advice was that production of the Big Swinger and the Swinger black-and-white, low-priced cameras was discontinued early-1970.

The **Bell & Howell** announcement of a slight recession in Net Sales but slightly higher income for 1970 was accompanied by the advice that their Training and Education Group continued to produce good results: that Consumer Products made satisfactory progress in an increasingly competitive market thanks to some innovative new products: that Business Equipment almost held its own in earnings and laid the ground for the resumption of profit growth: that Audio-Visual and Special Products increased profits on its educational lines but reduced earnings in special product areas more than offset these gains: that Electronics & Instruments continued to suffer from a badly depressed market environment: that the International Group moved ahead to new highs in both sales and earnings as well in their expectations for the future.

The Audio-Visual and Special Products Group was further mentioned with the advice that it had introduced, mid-1970, the 1500 series Autoload 16mm soundprojector. One unique feature, the Directamotion film advance control, allows the operator to advance the film frame by frame for analytical study of any segment in a motion picture. Early in 1971 they had entered the market with the Bell & Howell Attaché 35mm Sound Filmstrip Projection System, a portable, special-purpose unit for industrial customers. The design was fully contained with a built-in screen and sound filmstrip mechanism which could be used to present a synchronised audio and visual sales or training message in individual or small group situations.

In the Special Products Group, they again acknowledged the excellent relationship which they enjoyed with the Polaroid Corporation for whom they manufactured the Colorpak II and other cameras.

The Consumer Products Group had been established in 1970 and was responsible for product development, engineering and sales and distribution in the USA of all amateur photographic and audio tape equipment and software. In 1970, too, sales and earnings increased in the retail photographic segment of the business. The important Christmas buying season, when about one-third of annual consumer purchases were made, was more satisfactory than in the previous year. Other news was that the Slide Cube projector system, first marketed in 1970, successfully gained an important place in the slide projector market during 1970. Every expectation was held that this unit would continue to meet a fine response from the consumer.

Consumer products introduced during the year included the unique Auto-8 movie cassette projector system. With this fully-automatic system Regular 8 and Super 8 movie film was loaded into film cassettes which are used to show, retrieve, index and store the film. Major international projector manufacturers had decided to adapt this under licence for their own equipment designs.

It was announced at the same time that in 1971 they would introduce the Canon F-1 35mm single-lens-reflex still camera. This had a system of fine lenses, interchangeable viewfinders, automatic flash, electric motor drive and other accessories which provided maximum versatility for the advanced amateur and professional photographer.

The Electronics and Instruments Group was advised as having experienced a year of consolidation and re-direction, the Control Products Division as having experienced good sales and profit improvement. The Electronics Materials Division, a large supplier of high contrast chromium photoplates, had considerably expanded its facilities. The Business Equipment Group again moved ahead in most sectors in spite of marginally lower earnings, with microimagery products exhibiting special strength and promise for the future. It has also introduced the Director II Recorder, a heavy duty, 16mm microfilm recorder. In the Copier Division, optimism was entertained about the substantial growth potential which existed for its recently introduced, high-speed electrostatic copiers which had received excellent market acceptance. A final point made was that the year had been a strong one for their overseas operations, both sales and profits well above prior years, strength being especially evident in audio-visual products, Phillipsburg inserters, microfilm recorders, with a special growth opportunity seen in the difficult consumer photographic market.

The Photo Products Division of the **GAF Corporation** was noticed in the statement accompanying the reduced figures, for both Sales and Net Income, first, with the advice that it had not matched the growth rates of previous years. This factor, in combination with continuing start-up costs to produce new sensitised products, had exerted an adverse effect on earnings. It was further advised that sales had been influenced by consumer reluctance to spend in a year of unsettled monetary questions plus the heavy reduction in the Government's photographic expenditures. Plant production problems had also restricted their ability to meet fully customer requirements for certain products. During the year, however, their photo group management strengthened basic operations, improved manufacturing efficiency and re-directed efforts into higher-volume, more profitable areas.

In the Consumer Photo Division, increased sale of photographic film and hardgoods had improved the company's position in the industry. Domestic film sales, bolstered by the new GAF Colour Print film and a concerted television advertising schedule, had been well ahead of the previous year. The line of GAF slide projectors also benefited from increased advertising and promotion.

GAF View-Master three-dimensional viewers and stereo reels had not reached the sales success of the previous year when special 'Moon shot' packets received enthusiastic acceptance, but the new GAF Talking View-Master viewer and reels had achieved their sales forecast. The designation of GAF as the official film of Disneyland at Anaheim, California, in October of 1970, and the soon-to-be-completed Disney World near Orlando, Florida, had opened new sales horizons for all GAF consumer photo products. The GAF Disney agreement provided for some 55 retail outlets at the vacation lands, these being expected to attract more than seventeen million visitors annually.

An unusual event was the presentation by GAF to the White House with specially designed GAF View-Master Presidential Chests to be given to foreign dignitaries as souvenirs of their visits to the USA. These chests contained sixty reels of three-dimensional colour photographs of 'Americana' from each of the fifty States and were accepted by Mrs Nixon in the White House library.

The Industrial Photo Division was stated to have been affected by the cut-back in Federal spending, this causing lower Government sales, but both graphic and medical X-Ray items, both important segments of the product line, made significant advances. In both instances the GAF rate of sales growth was greater than the overall industry. Industrial X-Ray products, however, were affected by the sluggish general economy and reduced Federal defence outlays. Sales to professional studios, photo-finishers and commercial photographic supply houses were reduced by technical and production problems encountered in the introduction of new colour film and paper products. One of the principal costs inherent in these operations was stated to be scrap charges in perfecting these highly complex products. Intensive efforts, however, were being directed towards the solution of these problems primarily in the coating areas of the Binghampton, New York, plant. Progress had also been made by better utilisation of manpower and resources, also by eliminating obsolete equipment and processes.

Sales of medical X-Ray films benefited from the introduction of a new, improved GAF-X film, also a new dental film, polyester-based, and able to withstand high temperature processing, were marketed successfully. The graphic arts area's increased sales could be largely attributed to new, high definition GAF lithographic films on polyester and acetate bases. New products introduced for the professional photo market included COM film (Computer Output Microfilm), a new emulsion system for the identification and charge card markets, an improved colour print paper for photofinishing and the school photography field and a new colour paper processor to fill the needs of small to intermediate size photo laboratories.

The Industrial Photo Division also re-evaluated its low volume, low profit products, eliminating many of these from its catalogue. Additionally, a number of improved production systems, control techniques and silver recovery methods were developed and installed to reduce operating expenditures. The Business Systems Division was affected by the business austerity programmes of the year and could not contend with the drastic cutbacks in aerospace, automotive and general business spending.

The market for diazo equipment fell well below that of the previous year. Additionally, increased manufacturing costs could only be partially offset by price increases in diazo materials and machines. The GAF 365 and 310 Rollfeed Diazoprinters, featuring unique convenience devices, were introduced during the last quarter and customer response indicated improved sales for the coming year. In the electrostatic copier line, the company was able to improve its overall marketing position mainly because of the introduction of the GAF 800 Copier/Duplicator, a high-speed machine which affords low-cost, top-quality reproduction. An expanded distribution system was noticed in this context as having grown from ninety-five to one hundred and forty dealers. Full market potential for the machine was, consequently, envisaged. Final points made were that GAF's sales abroad were 25% higher, this not only helping to compensate for weaker home sales but also extending GAF brands into several new territories.

Net Sales of **Pako Corporation** for 1970 were at a new high level, and the summit of a steadily firming trend which began some years previously, but Income was down. It was advised that they had sought to introduce several major new products for which considerable interest had been generated. In order to expedite delivery they had compressed engineering and production schedules. But these were too tight, especially on the two solid state photographic printers. Additionally, field tests of prototype models disclosed changes which were necessary for optimum performance and to minimize maintenance and servicing costs. Many of these changes were made whilst products were on the production line, thus creating adverse expense variations and delays.

Other unfavourable factors named, which were outside the company's control, included the nation-wide truck strike, premature rumours of technological changes and the much-publicised economic slow-down. Adjustments made during the year, however, were envisaged as reversing the trend in the forthcoming year. The acquisition of Photopic Systems, Inc, a major Pako distributor serving the New York trade area, had been achieved and consequently extended their marketing capabilities. This company had experienced rapid sales growth since its inception four years ago and a profit contribution was anticipated in the forthcoming year.

The company had also contracted for the supply of Pakon mounts with a nationally recognised plastic fabricator. They were, consequently, assured of sufficient quantities of these popular mounts on schedule as they had the facilities and the necessary expertise. This arrangement was foreseen as proving advantageous for the coming year. Other advice was that Pakomp, a computerised invoicing, pricing and transaction control-system which they had been developing with Honeywell, Inc, was on schedule and field testing was to begin. Sales and profits from Pako Photo and Filmshops continued to encourage expansion into more Minnesota communities. Overseas, sales of Pako equipment had reached record levels and they were studying the feasibility of expanding their production facilities abroad as these markets represented excellent growth potential for the future. As regards labour relations, it was advised that they had successfully negotiated a two-year contract with the International Association of Machinists and Aerospace Workers.

New products featured in the Annual Report included the Pakorol CTX which processes black-and-white film, in rolls or cut sheets, with high quality control and suitable for the smallest studio or the largest photographic laboratory: the Mach I Colour Printer capable of high-speed, quality colour printing from the popular 126 cartridge size film, for high volume printing without increasing the consumers' cost: new paper processors which combined increased capacity with the innovation of air-drying, and which permitted adding volume without added labour: the Pakopro, described as the ultimate in print processing for the portrait studio, which processes a single-strand of colour print material up to eleven inches wide, its low cost putting never-before-possible processing into the hands of the professional photographer: a versatile new small processor for Kodacolor Type Film, the smallest model built yet, only nine feet long, yet combining all the features for the highest professional quality with low operating cost: a Pakon mounter capable of handling up to one hundred and sixty slides per minute and of dating, numbering and imprinting the mounts for customers' convenience.

New products in the Medical and Industrial X-Ray field also featured included the Pakorol XU, a X-Ray film processing system for hospitals, clinics and offices which processes and dries film in ninety seconds: the Pakorol Super G, of which there are seven models, and which cover both litho film and colour-separating negatives, for graphic arts requiring film processing, and which, also, has a handy control panel: the Pakorol GT-12, a specialised processor for phototypesetting film and paper, and which provides substantial cost savings, superior image quality and faster processing.

A final point made in the same context was that never before had the company had so many new products.

M. DUFFY

BLACK AND WHITE PHOTOGRAPHY
Rise and Fall of the Monobath

The processing of photographic material by a single solution is no new idea. The silver chloride paper photographs produced by Nicéphore Niepce in 1816 were darkened by light and fixed with nitric acid, so only one solution was involved. Indeed, the bitumen of Judea process which was 'developed' by a solvent consisting of oil of lavender and white petroleum, likewise used one solution, though the French 'révélateur' would better fit the process than the English word 'developer'. However, the daguerreotype soon followed with its mercury vapour development and subsequent fixation, first with common salt and later with thiosulphate, so the earlier simplicity was lost. Of course, in a sense the old POP paper could be said to have monobath processing. However, as a rule the word 'monobath' is considered to refer to solution for combined fixation and development of silver halide materials.

Experiments had already been made with combined developers and fixers before the end of the nineteenth century, but early workers found many practical difficulties. A small amount of hypo or other fixing agent in a developer can severely reduce the emulsion speed, and in those days any appreciable speed drop could make the process impractical. A communication from W.D. Richmond appeared in the issue of the *British Journal of Photography* for 20 December 1889 and in this he described the following monobath.

Solution 1	Silver nitrate	100 grains in 5 ounces of water.
" 2	Ammonium thiocyanate	240 grains in 5 ounces of water.
" 3	Sodium thiosulphate	240 grains in 5 ounces of water.
" 4	Pyrogallol	10% solution.
" 5	Ammonia	20% solution.

Take 1 drachm of each solution and add sufficient water to cover a ¼-plate. At that date the thiosulphate would be crystalline and the ammonia would be domestic-type ammonium hydroxide.

Richmond regarded this monobath as a photographic curiosity, pointing out a high fog level, silver deposits, and considerable increase in development time. The basic fault was that separate solutions could work better than combined ones and, in essence, this still tends to be true today.

As new developing agents were produced, various workers tried them in monobath formulations. It was believed that the heavy loss of emulsion speed was caused by fixation of exposed silver halide or development centres before the developer could act. This produced a mental picture of a race between developer and fixer, so to confer advantage on the former the developer concentration was often made relatively high and the pH alkalinity raised. Plates that developed quickly, such as those used for lantern slides, proved more amenable to single-solution processing than faster materials, and, as the emulsion speeds of films and plates continued to rise, it became increasingly difficult to produce well-balanced monobaths to use with them. Various organic developing agents were employed including hydroquinone, paraphenylenediamine, metol, Amidol and para-aminophenol. The literature is somewhat obscured by the use of a multitude of synonyms and trade names for various developing agents and combinations of agents, such as Ortol (hydroquinone and orthomethylaminophenol) and Edinol (orthohydroxymethyl-para-amino-phenol hydrochloride) but in general almost every new agent was tried in a monobath. The first MQ monobath was formulated by Raymond towards the end of 1909. A considerable step forward was taken by Cremier in 1911. He considered the monobath action as the resultant of fixation being greatest in unexposed halide and, logically if obviously, development being fastest in the most heavily exposed regions. These actions, together with the fixer acting as a restrainer, were held to explain speed loss, soft gradation with underexposure and high contrast with overexposure. He preferred amidol (metadiaminophenol hydrochloride) as needing less alkali and tending to produce lower contrast.

Amidol	10·0gm
Sodium sulphite (anhydrous)	50·0gm
Sodium thiosulphate (crystalline)	20·0gm
Water to	1litre

Sheppard and Mees pointed out in 1907 that, in alkaline developing solutions containing low concentrations of hypo, development was normal deep in the emulsion, the modifying influence of the solvent being greatest on the surface. Two 'ready-made' monobaths were marketed in this era, namely Eikonal F (a pyrogallol type) and in Britain, Develofix (reviewed by *The British Journal of Photography* in 1913).

In 1914 Otsuki and Sudzuki devised a useful MQ monobath actually the Lumière name, Metoquinone, was used to describe the combination of two molecules of metol with one of hydroquinone. At the time this was considered advanced and the use of moderate alkalinity, i.e. 5gm/litre of sodium hydroxide together with sulphite as a preservative, did produce a reasonably stable solution. Another Japanese worker, Hashimoto, in 1923 modified this formula to produce variations to suit different materials as shown in the table below:

	Rapid plates	Negative film	Papers
Metoquinone	10gm	10gm	10gm
Sodium hydroxide	20gm	15gm	10gm
Sodium sulphite, anhydrous	80gm	75gm	70gm
Sodium thiosulphate, anhydrous	190gm	180gm	190gm
Water to 1litre			

It will be noted that the hypo concentration was relatively high, it having been found that under such conditions the alkali could also be increased without unreasonably adverse effects. Various experiments were made with different alkalis; in particular the Lumière brothers became fond of the use of trisodium phosphate which was subsequently tried by several workers. A formula quoted for many years and using this alkali is:

Sodium sulphite (anhydrous)	40·0gm
Amidol	5·0gm
Sodium phosphate (tribasic)	20·0gm
Sodium thiosulphate (crystalline)	25·0gm
Water to make 1litre	

Several interesting ideas appeared around 1940, such as the use of copper sulphate by the German firm of Schering to allow a carbonate to replace hydroxide as alkali, while Ham proposed the use of anthranilix acid or guanidine anthrilate as developer aids, the reason for this is obscure.

One of the basic faults of monobaths is that alkalis tend to soften emulsions and make them swell, with consequent damage. Alburger proposed aluminate buffering to inhibit swelling and mitigate softening. His formula was as follows:

Sodium sulphite (anhydrous)	50·0gm
Hydroquinone	15·0gm
Sodium hydroxide	30·0gm
Potassium alum	40·0gm
Potassium bromide	7·0gm
Water to make 1litre	

Various modifications of Alburger's formula were used for special purposes. For example a hydroquinone version was employed for processing positive film in 90 seconds, a glycin adaptation for aerial film in 4 minutes and a metol-glycin formulation, claimed to be very stable, could process aerial film in 2½ minutes. Zinc sulphate and lead nitrate were also tried for buffering by the German team following Alburger and the conclusions reached were that metallate buffering could improve stability, reduce staining, and help towards the reduction of speed loss. By this time monobaths had reached a stage where it was considered that speed loss could be less than with the fine-grain developers of that time.

A period of intense development followed when the US Air Force sponsored investigations. The method was to alter ingredients in a systematic manner until the optimum balance was achieved for aerial film. In America 40in wide rolls are used, the emulsion resembling the normal high-speed panchromatic type but being capable of a higher maximum density. Ham's guanidine anthrilate and other ingredients were found to be ineffective and, in 1953, H.S. Keelan summarised the effects of investigations following the Alburger system. Most monobaths faults were said to have been eliminated but a speed loss of about 40% remained. Some typical formulae are as follows:

	212	365	315	348
Metol	1·5gm	1·9gm	10·0gm	33·5gm
Sodium sulphite, anhydrous	25·0gm	33·0gm	50·0gm	50·0gm
Hydroquinone	13·5gm	17·1gm	40·0gm	15·0gm
Potassium alum	5·0gm	20·0gm	20·0gm	20·0gm
Sodium hydroxide	9·0gm	16·0gm	35·0gm	30·0gm
Sodium thiosulphate	30·0gm	60·0gm	110·0gm	50·0gm
Benzotriazol	1·0gm	1·0gm	—	—
0·5% 6-nitrobenziminazole	—	—	20·0ml	20·0ml
Potassium bromide	3·35gm	—	—	—
Gluconic acid	0·1gr	—	—	—
Water to	1litre	1litre	1litre	1litre
pH	11·2	11·3	11·55	11·35

Formula 212 is intended for slow contact papers (2–3 minutes processing time), 365 is for fast bromide papers

(3 minutes), 315 is for negative emulsions of Aero Super XX type (3 minutes), while 348 is intended for machine processing of the same film (which then takes 10 minutes).

Exhaustion characteristics of these monobaths were quite good, but Keelan was not satisfied and decided to try increasing the effective film speed. His ideas, like those of previous workers in this field, were basically to find a developing agent sufficiently active to overcome the depressing effect of the fixer. Triaminophenol trihydrochloride was tried but proved too susceptible to oxidation also with sugars as preservatives. Phenidone proved to be the answer, as with so many other photographic developers. In 1957 Keelan published the formula for Monobath 438, which was claimed to have eliminated the previous speed loss, except with Panatomic-X.

Monobath 438

Hydroquinone	15·0gm
Sodium sulphite (anhydrous)	50·0gm
Phenidone	10·0gm
Potassium alum	18·0gm
Sodium hydroxide	18·0gm
Sodium thiosulphate	60·0gm
Water to 1litre	

A more economical monobath is FX6a, one of the useful FX series which has been published in the *British Journal of Photography Annual* for many years.

FX-6a

Sodium sulphite (anhydrous)	50·0gm
Hydroquinone	12·0gm
Phenidone	1·0gm
Sodium hydroxide	10·0gm
Sodium thiosulphate	90·0gm
Water to 1litre	

The hypo concentration may be varied between 70 and 125gm/litre, the latter limit giving as soft a result as is likely to be required. If harder gradation is required than is conferred with 70gm/litre (which could happen with process materials) then the hydroquinone can be increased to 15 or 17gm. See also page 231.

Meanwhile, theoretical investigations continued elsewhere, and in 1953 Clarke, Milner, and Gomez-Ibanez showed that the printing density of a monobath-processed negative was less than that produced by a conventionally processed negative with the same amount of silver. The hypothesis of partial physical development in monobath processing has been discounted by both Jaenicke and Barnes. It is considered that unexposed silver halide could move to development centres and be reduced there to silver. Since normally developed silver could be described as resembling bundled fibres, somewhat like cotton-wool, the silver from migrated halide could be deposited in the interstices to form the characteristic sharp-edged but relatively coarse grain of monobaths.

Other fixing agents have been suggested as substitutes for or additions to the usual thiosulphate. Organic sulphur compounds (2-mercaptopyridene or 2-mercaptopyrimidines) were mentioned by Dreywood and later a considerable number of other fixing agents were described by Haist, King and Bassage. It is interesting to note that the original formula of Richmond included a thiocyanate, and the use of potassium thiocyanate plus thiosulphate has been reported to work well. Another idea was to add an organic amine to a monobath; for example ethylenediamine was said by J.S. Goldhammer to permit a high development rate with only moderate solution alkalinity, so that grain was comparatively fine.

Fine Grain Monobath

Sodium bisulphite	50·0gm
Amidol	10·0gm
Ethykebeduanube (85 to 88%)	32·0ml
6-Nitrobenzimidazole (0·5%)	40·0ml

Hydroquinone	3·3gm
Sodium thiocyanate	10·0gm
Sodium thiosulphate (crystalline)	60·0gm
Water to make 1litre	

Commercial monobaths have frequently been announced with much blowing of trumpets, but despite the undeniable advantages, the drawbacks eventually proved greater. One of the first was called just 'Monobath', and originated in the Pratt Laboratories in 1939, but soon vanished from the scene.

The obvious advantage of any monobath is that the processes proceed to completion, so that the exact duration of processing does not matter and there is even considerable latitude in temperature. The idea of pouring in one solution and producing a perfectly processed negative, without any chance of failure, and with no need of accurate working, has obvious attractions to the amateur. Unfortunately, since the contrast is pre-set no allowance can be made for type of film, or subject, unless modifications are possible.

In 1959 Unibath was introduced in the USA and the makers, the Cormac Corporation of New York, met the problem of matching material and monobath by producing eight varieties of the latter. For example, CC1 was for standard films normally exposed, CC2 for high-speed films with barely adequate exposure, and CC3 for papers. The last of these proved unsuccessful, at least with British papers, since emulsion speed was reduced by a factor of four, and contrast also dropped to an extent which could not be predicted for any specific grade.

The film developers allowed the use of the nominal speed rating and gave good acutance but the emulsion became very fragile and subject to reticulation. This weakness appears general in monobaths of this period, possibly because the Alburger aluminate buffer system fails at high pH values. The basic trouble is that any time saved in processing is lost in the longer drying time needed by the swollen emulsion. Again, though the time and temperature of the monobath are not critical, the temperature of the washing water must be carefully watched to guard against reticulation.

Other monobaths proved somewhat similar, though each had its individual characteristics. Monophen, based on Phenidone and hydroquinone with potassium alum buffering, was intended mainly for Ilford films, and so was required in only one formulation. However, there was some emulsion softening, full film speed was not achieved, and grain was high compared with ID-11 and such developers.

Monotenal, from Tetenal, was different from other formulae and met the compatability problem by being balanced for films below ASA250. The solution was slightly greenish, pH about 13, and almost certainly contained an organic amine. As usual, acutance was good and grain comparatively high, however emulsion speed was not only retained but with some films a useful increase could be obtained. Unfortunately, the emulsion was softened.

Simprol, from May and Baker, could be adjusted for contrast by adding more solvent, potassium thiosulphate, which was supplied in two sachets. This allowed three variations of contrast, so giving a degree of control, though losing some of the desirable simplicity which so attracts the novice-photographer. Again, acutance was high, grain not fine, and the emulsion was softened. Also, contrast fell at low temperatures and some precipitates, characteristic of glycin monobaths, could appear on the film at high temperatures.

To date one monobath has been marketed which solves, partially, the problem of film hardening. This was Develofix from the FR Corporation. It was intended mainly for Panatomic-X film and worked reasonably well but the hardener made the solution so unstable that it had to be used very quickly and storage of the mixed solution was not possible.

In general it must be conceded that no monobath can offer the same advantageous combination of qualities as the separate developer and fixer sequence. The problem of predetermined contrast has been well met by restricting the films with which a formula can be used, or producing several variations of a monobath, or by adjustment of solvent content. After all, commercial development at the D&P level often allows no contrast control. The emulsion softening is probably the biggest drawback, and so far no really satisfactory solution has been found. Emulsion speed maintenance has been achieved, especially by the use of pyrazolidones, but it must not be forgotten that those same developing agents can confer a speed increase of about 60% in separate developers, and it is this enhanced speed which should serve as the basis for comparison. The balance of sensitometric characteristics is extremely good in most modern proprietary developers and no monobath has yet achieved quite the same standard. Of course, good results were produced during the heyday of monobaths, but usually by experts who would have been at least as successful with conventional processing.

Suggestions have been made that a monobath could be followed by a hardener. This is certainly a partial answer to several problems, but at once spoils the whole single-solution concept. Indeed, this idea of split-processing, whether for hardening or using the monobath as a self-limiting developer followed by a fixer, could almost be construed as an admission of weakness in present monobath knowledge. Many monobaths have quietly vanished away but there may well be a subsequent renaissance if the hardening problem can be solved. The best hope of this would seem to lie with the organic hardeners, such as aldehydes, since these work well at the high pH values where metallates become ineffective—above pH 6·5 chromium and aluminium compounds are of little use with photographic gelatin. A vast range of aldehydes have been suggested as hardening compounds, and most work by forming intermolecular bridges—with formaldehyde, for example, methylene bridges are present). Some of the compounds would be imcompatible with monobaths but the dialdehydes have possibilities. If we accept the concept that, at the iso electric point, the hardener combines with amino groups of the lysine derivatives, this gives a starting point for investigation.

It is only fair to add that, whilst the deposition of silver or sludging was dismissed earlier in this article as being of little consequence—and it does occur also in developers like Promicrol and Ultrafin, and other developers containing solvents even so mild a one as sulphite—some authorities, including Haist, consider it more severely detrimental in a monobath. Certainly the action does free thiosulphate at a time when developing agents are relatively depleted, and

this could unbalance the monobath. In rare instances sludging can occur during processing, deposits forming on the film, and this is obviously awkward. Organic silver complexing agents could be used in place of thiosulphate, but here one meets the problem of cost. A sequestering or chelating agent for silver could solve this problem and von König and Pfeiffenschneider found that as low a concentration as 50mg/litre of a 2-mercapto-1,3,4-thiadiazole derivative would keep silver in solution. However, much depends on the reduction nuclei present.

It is not likely that a manufacturer would produce a general-purpose film specifically for use with a monobath (say by prehardening) but specific-task materials could be designed for compatability with single-solution processing. For example, micro-film is particularly suitable, especially when used with mechanised processing having controlled replenishment. Canon have a complete system, while Agfa and Cormac produce monobaths (Dokufix and CC7 respectively) specifically tailored for microfilms. Again, monobaths for motion picture films and even X-ray films have been devised, nor can the single-solution print processes be ignored. An outstandingly successful monobath system is the Polaroid-Land technique of silver diffusion, and further developments can be expected in this area.

The slow improvement in general-purpose monobaths continued from before 1900 to the commercial exploitation stage in the 1960s, then these single-solution products vanished as photographers found the disadvantages outweighed the merits. However, this fall from favour need not be permanent. It is possible for the hardening and sludging problems to be overcome. A particular problem is in designing a monobath which is effective with many types of film, in order to achieve a sufficient volume of production. It is possible that the present trend of amalgamation between firms, and the rationalisation of materials, will eventually reduce customers' choice to the point where specific tailoring for a few emulsions becomes more feasible. It is certain that as long as photographers enjoy devising and improving developers, they will strive also towards a more perfect monobath.

The following books and articles have proved useful and could be consulted generally:-

The History of Photography, Gernsheim
Photographic Chemistry, Glafkides, Vol. 1
Monobath Manual, Grout Haist
Investigations on the Theory of the Photographic Process, Sheppard and Mees
Seventy Years of Progress in Photographic Monobaths, Brit J Phot 23 Jan 1959. A.A. Newman
Progress in Monobaths, J Phot Sc, Vol 15, 1967. A.A. Newman
V. Cremier, Brit J Phot **58**, 1911
Brit J Phot **61**, 1914
Brit J Phot **71**, 1924

NEVILLE MAUDE

Toning Ilfobrom

This data from Ilford Limited relating to Ilfobrom paper should be found of more general application with modern bromide papers.

There are a number of methods available for red-toning or dyeing prints. They fall in the following clearly defined categories:

(1) Sulphide and selenium toners giving brown to purple-black images. It is not possible to produce red tones by these methods.

(2) Metal toners which convert the silver image into either a coloured insoluble silver salt or a double salt with another metal.

The most successful results will probably be obtained with one of these methods.

(3) Dye toning and colour developing methods are des-

cribed in the *Focal Encyclopedia of Photography*. They are complicated techniques and the images tend to fade on exposure to light.

The following two methods from the second category have been tried on Ilfobrom and of the two the former method appears to give the most pleasing results.

GOLD TONING

An Ilfobrom print is first bleached in the following bath:

Bleach:

Potassium ferricyanide	50·0gm
Potassium bromide	50·0gm
Water to make	1 litre

After bleaching (5min) the print is washed for 5–10 minutes and then treated with the thiourea toner.

Thiourea toner:

Solution A:	Sodium hydroxide	160·0gm
	Water to make	1 litre
Solution B:	Thiourea	40·0gm
	Water to make	1 litre

For use, add 25ml solution (a) to approximately 500ml of water, then add 25ml solution (b) and make up to 1litre with water.

The print is treated with the toner until no further action takes place about 4–5 minutes and then washed for 30min in running water. The print may then be toned in the following solution:

Gold toner:

Ammonium thiocyanate	10·0gm
Gold sodium chloride	0·5gm
Water to make	500·0ml

Dissolve the two components separately in small amounts of water and mix by adding the gold solution gradually to that of the thiocyanate. After toning the print must be rinsed, fixed and washed for 30min.

Note: The gold toner may be applied to the print by swabbing on to the moist print with cotton wool, in which case the cost is not more than a few pence per whole-plate print. Toning may take 5–10min. The current cost of gold sodium chloride is about £1 per gram. One supplier is Hopkins & Williams, Freshwater Road, Chadwell Heath, Essex.

NICKEL/DIMETHYL GLYOXINE TONER

The method given in the *Focal Encyclopedia of Photography* is typical and gives pink-red images on Ilfobrom which do not compare with the gold toner for depth of tone in the shadows. In tests carried out here there was some staining of the margin and the highlights of the print by this method. In normal nickel toning the print is first immersed in the following bleaching bath, in which the toner converts the silver image into silver and nickel ferrocyanide.

Nickel nitrate	50·0gm
Potassium citrate	300·0gm
Citric acid	25·0gm
Formalin, 40% solution	100·0ml
Water to make	1000·0ml

Just before use, 5 parts of this solution are mixed with 1 part 15% potassium ferricyanide. After bleaching, the print is immersed in a 5% sodium thiosulphate solution for 5–10min.

For bright red tones the print is then toned with a dimethyl glyoxime toner:

Dimethyl glyoxime, saturated solution (7–8%) in alcohol	10 parts
Ammonia solution, 0·880	1 part
Sodium hydroxide, 5% solution	1 part
Water to make	100 parts

Final washing in changes of 0·1% acetic acid solution completes the process.

For violet tones the nickel-toned print may be immersed in a 25% solution of ferric alum containing 0·5% of sulphuric acid and 10% of potassium bromide. For bluish-green tones the original black-and-white image is bleached in the nickel bleacher, washed and immersed for 5min in 5% ferric chloride, followed by hydrochloric acid diluted 1:6. The print or transparency is then washed in several changes of 1% citric acid, fixed in 5% sodium thiosulphate solution, and washed again in eight to ten changes of 1% citric acid.

YELLOW-BROWN TONES

Thioantimonate toner:
The image is converted to silver bromide by use of the following bleach bath:

Potassium ferricyanide	50·0gm
Potassium bromide	50·0gm
Water to make	1 litre

The prints are washed in running water for twice the time it takes to remove the yellow stain (about 10min) and then re-developed in the following formulation.

Working solution:

Sodium thioantimonate	10·0gm
Ammonia (0·880)	1·0ml
Water to make	1 litre

This toner gives warm, orange-brown tones.

Toning with metallic ferrocyanides
The silver image can be replaced by insoluble metallic ferrocyanides to give different colours, and this can be achieved in two ways. One method is to bleach the image in a 5% potassium ferricyanide solution, to which a little ammonia or sodium carbonate may be added to speed the process. The print should then be washed and placed in a solution of the salt of the metal, and the coloured image will then be formed. If the metal forms a ferrocyanide less soluble than the silver ferrocyanide which it replaces, a halide should be present, but if the soluble metal salt is a halide then fixing after toning is required to remove the silver halide formed.

A more popular method is to have the potassium ferricyanide and the metal salt in the same solution, which in most cases means the addition of a citrate, oxalate, tartrate or similar compound to prevent immediate precipitation. The most common is a solution of neutral potassium citrate (also called tribasic potassium citrate). Sequestrenes may also be used. The most frequently used metal is copper, and the single-bath method is by far the most popular, since four atoms of silver produce three molecules of copper ferrocyanide, whereas in the two-bath method they would produce only one.

As with most toners, washing should be adequate and the toner must be stored in two separate solutions, otherwise its life would be too short.

Solution A:

Copper sulphate	25v0gm
Potassium citrate (neutral)	110·0gm
Water to	1 litre

Solution B:

Potassium ferrocyanide	20·0gm
Potassium citrate (neutral)	110·0gm
Water to	1 litre

For use, mix A and B 1:1.

If toning is incomplete, silver ferrocyanide will be present which cannot be removed by fixation, due to interaction between the components of the image, resulting in the virtual disappearance of both. In consequence, either toning must be complete or the results will not be permanent unless another method of toning is used to make the residual silver ferrocyanide permanent.

A number of other metals can be used which will yield different colours. For example:

Lead, *white*
Cadmium, *white*
Titanium, *yellow*
Vanadium, *orange-yellow*
Uranium, *red* to *red-brown*
Nickel, *red-brown*
Cobalt (single bath), *violet-red*
Cobalt (two bath), *cyan*
Iron, *prussian blue*

Obviously there is no point in producing a white image on white base paper, but the white images can be treated to produce compounds of other colours.

The cadmium ferrocyanide can be turned to yellow sulphide toning, and if this is done without prior removal of silver ferrocyanide, the mixture of silver and cadmium sulphides will produce a yellow-brown tone. The lead ferrocyanide image may be converted to chrome yellow (lead chromate) in an alkaline chromate or bichromate solution.

Other changes are possible, e.g. nickel ferrocyanide may be treated with an alcoholic solution of 1% dimethylglyoxine made alkaline by the addition of a little sodium hydroxide, but this solution can be destroyed by even a weak acid.

ILFORD LIMITED

COLOUR PHOTOGRAPHY

The almost explosive evolution in technology, of all kinds, and in science and its applications which we have seen in the last ten years have made us blase and nothing now astonishes us. Think of the landing of the first man on the moon—we were then almost unconcerned about the second lunar expedition. The dramatic return to earth of Apollo 13 made us shudder, but has been quickly forgotten!

Colour photography continues its successful progress, the process is improving, mechanising of operations in colour printing has already reached a point unimaginable a few years ago. Nevertheless, in the last year, there have been no novelties and the classic colour processes remain the most important. We are arriving at the point where all the techniques in emulsion making and processing are reaching a common denominator, the fact which has certainly been necessitated by economic demands. On the other hand, the silver-dye-bleach process, Cibachrome, has gained ground, and a second firm is now setting out along this path. Colour reversal processes based on chromogenic development have not evolved. Kodak, who lead the dance in this sector, retain a definite advantage with the E-4 process adopted by other manufacturers (Fuji); and the classic Kodachrome process has not yet lost its prestige.

In the negative-positive sector, self-masking films have practically supplanted unmasked emulsions. Compatability with the C-22 process—also from Kodak—is being adhered to by a growing number of competitors in designing their materials (Fuji, Tura, 3M, GAF). In this sector technology is directing itself towards speeding up the processing procedure, a point on which Kodak is again showing the way. RC-type colour papers (resin coated) are tempting a growing number of manufacturers, again pulled along by Kodak.

Agfa-Gevaert
The *Agfachrome Professional* (Type L and F) reversal films are now fully on the market and their obvious qualities in colour rendering are making them rapidly popular amongst professional photographers. There have been no changes in the *Agfacolor* (CT18 and derivatives) for amateur use. The *Duplichrome D13* sheet films permit slide copying with an exceptional preservation of the original colours. Besides this they allow industrial graphic processes to be rationalised in the interests of efficiency. *Agfacolor Professional* (L and S) is an improved type of Agfacolor CNS, with better masking. This is available like Agfachrome Professional in all the usual formats, 35mm—120 and in sheet film.

The silver-dye-bleach process has also reached a mature stage in its development at Agfa, and an experimental production on a limited scale is already in existence. The launching of a new colour paper based on this system may be near. It is said that the results are outstanding and, according to the technicians of this firm, are superior in quality to anything currently available. . .

Although leaving the exact sphere of colour emulsions, it is necessary to note the exceptional colour derivatives made possible by *Agfacontour Professional*, whether used in scientific photography (astronomy, radiography, physics, electron microscopy, geology), techniques, graphic arts, textile printing, aerial photography or artistic. The material is assured of a brilliant future just as much with the advanced amateur photographer as it is with the professional.

Gevaert-Agfa are producing a new professional film for positive colour prints; *Gevacolor Print type 9.85* designed for use in colour television and the motion picture industry.

CIBA-Photochemicals, FA
The silver-dye-bleach process, pulled out of the doldrums thanks to the pioneering work of this Bâsle firm, has definitely acquired the right to the rank of a true photographic process. The outstanding qualities of the *Cibachrome* material (resistance to the attack from the environment—especially from light—fidelity of colour rendering, dimensional stability, high resolving power) are leading to an increasing diversity of application in scientific, industrial and display photography. Besdies *Cibachrome Print (CCP)*, a positive material for reflection copying, *Cibachrome Transparent*, Display (CCT-D) makes possible the preparation of transparencies of almost any dimension. It is available in rolls of up to 108cm in width. It may be remembered that the Cibachrome process has an undeniable advantage for copying, since it makes it possible starting from the original transparency, to obtain a literally perfect reproduction without having to go through a reversal process.

Fotochema (Czechoslovakia)
This dynamic Czech enterprise has marketed a new reversal material, replacing *Fomachrome D.16* which appeared in experimental batches about two years ago, the new material being *Fomachrome D.18* (50 ASA 18 DIN). It is expected to

be fully on the market during this current year in the usual format, 35mm, 120 and sheet film. Its colour rendering is good, fully up to western standards. Fomacolor (Type PN and PM, the latter being balanced for masked colour negatives) has been improved again, it is fully up to the standard of the papers encountered on the international market, according to the trials we have ourselves conducted. Filtration for the material has been specially designed to be compatible with the automatic printing machines manufactured in Switzerland by Gretag, a subsidiary of *CIBA*.

In addition, the translucent material on a plastic base called *Fomacolor Opale* is now fully available on the market. As to their negative unmasked colour film, it is probable that manufacture will be gradually discontinued. It may be remembered that Fotochema provides Orwo with its Orwocolor colour paper.

Forte (Hungary)
This manufacturer who prepares a very good colour paper called *Fortecolor Type 2*, has improved it once again. The *Fortecolor CN4 Type 3* is now available in all the usual formats and in rolls for automatic printers. The colour rendering is good and the whites are now really pure. Processing is identical with that of Agfacolor MCN111.

Fotokemika (Yugoslavia)
This firm, which has been working in close collaboration with Ferrania, has introduced onto the domestic market a reversal colour film *FK-Color RD17* (40 ASA, 17 DIN), as well as the masked negative material *FK:Color NM19*, which is similar to the old Ferrania-color negative material NM64. Production of colour materials by Fotokemika is not sufficient to allow export, but it is possible that their production capacity will increase to allow this. Their colour print paper is only available at the moment in rolls.

Foton (Poland)
This firm only supplies its domestic market and in small quantities, the one material, colour paper of the Agfacolor type.

Fuji Photo Film (Japan)
This energetic manufacturer has undertaken with some success the conquest of the european market; the reversal colour film Fujichrome R100, has already been favourably received by continental photographers. It is processed either according to Kodak E-4 or Fuji CR53. The masked negative material Fujicolor N100 is developed in the Kodak process C-22 or Fuji CN-15. It is resin-coated material and should be soon appearing in Europe. It may be emphasised that the quality of this Japanese material is first class and may be favourably compared with its competitors. It should be noted that Fujichrome R100 will soon be available in the 120 format. Also, Fuji have announced the iminent arrival of a colour print material.

GAF-ANSCO (USA)
The GAF-Color Slide film (Anscochrome) 64, 200 and 500 (these numbers indicating ASA speeds) are already well known to photographers. In particular, the last has appealed to a good number of experienced professional photographers as it is, at the moment, the only material on the market of this basic sensitivity and opens up wide possibilities in candid colour photography.

The main novelty from this firm is the appearance on the european market of their masked negative film *GAF Color Print Film*, 80 ASA, 20 DIN. This is developed in the Kodak

C-22 process and is at the moment available in 126 and 35mm formats. The matching colour paper is not, as we write, yet available in Europe, but the negative material can be easily printed on any masked colour paper.

It may be noted that Anscochrome 64, 200 and 500 are only made in daylight type. Tungsten types have disappeared. The reason for this is that nowadays most interior photographs are made with electronic flash or blue flash bulbs.

Kodak (USA and etc)
There have been whispers for some time that this powerful enterprise had something new up its sleeve, in particular a new unmasked colour negative film... Nothing of the sort has happened, however, and Kodacolor X and Ektacolor Professional go from strength to strength. However, a different type of novelty, particularly designed for professional laboratories has come to notice; this is the *Vericolor* process. In fact, this is basically a method of mechanised processing at a high temperature (38°C) of a negative colour film derived from Ektacolor Professional (CPF) and available in 666cm and sheet film sizes. A 35mm type is in preparation too. Processing commences with a pre-hardening bath and finishes with a hardener. The total processing time is 10min. The Ektachrome remain unchanged, but the selection has been enhanced by the addition of Type B (3,200°K artificial light balance) in 35mm. The RC (resin-coated) paper is now also on the market in Ektacolor (it was originally only made as Ektachrome reversal paper) in three grades: amateur, professional and commercial. The treatment of these papers with a synthetic resin has made possible a useful economy in treatment time because, since they retain less moisture, drying is much quicker. Since RC papers have a brilliant surface, drum-glazing is made unnecessary, and it is possible to dry prints by passing them through a high frequency dryer. One disadvantage—a small one they say, but a disadvantage nevertheless—is that the borders are noticeably less white than those of normal papers. This may explain the new fashion of borderless prints which can be justified by a gain in surface area, for the same price...

It should be mentioned that Kodak have also shown a video-colour printer which makes possible immediate inspection of the positive image from a negative to be printed. By its use choice of filters for colour printing are made much easier and the effect of changes in the colour balance can be seen in advance. A zoom lens allows very precise correction by allowing the operator to concentrate on important but small parts of the negative.

Konishiroku (Japan)
The marketing in Europe of photochemical products manufactured by Konishiroku and sold under their brand name *Sakura* now seems certain. Their production programme is is on a very large scale and three products are especially worthy of our attention.

The reversal film *Sakuracolor R-100* (100 ASA, 21 DIN) is available in 120 and 35mm format; the negative colour material *Sakuracolor N-100* (100 ASA, 21 DIN) are both balanced for daylight. Exact information on the properties of these materials is not available, but the reversal film is similar to those of 3M and Agfacolor, and the negative material (masked) is (probably) not compatible with C-22.

The third product, which may, up to now, be unique to Sakura is a film for two-colour radiography allowing colour pictures to be taken by X-rays: one layer on development generates a blue dye and the second a yellow dye. Each emulsion layer is' sensitive to X-radiations of a different energy band. Two successive exposures, one to 'soft' rays, and other to 'hard' rays make possible an exceedingly 'plastic' radiograph, in which the two colours appear alone or combined according to the composition and permeability of the medium (bone, cartridges, tissue). This should be a valuable aid in radiography.

Their positive colour paper is not yet available on the european market. In the motion picture sector Konishiroku produce Sakura Color Positive in 16 and 35mm gauges, as well as Sakura Color Reversal, TV, in 16mm; and there is also a Sakura Color Reversal (daylight type) for Super 8 (25 ASA).

Veb Orwo

This firm seems to have some difficulty in consistency of production: the new masked negative material *Orwocolor-Mask 19*, announced as a replacement of Mask 17, whose existence was very short, is not yet available, and amateur photographers loyal to the brand are continuing to use the earlier unmasked NC-16.

As regards reversal colour materials, *Orwochrome UT18*, which was introduced at photokina in 1968, is now on the market. As regards Orwochrome UT21 which the writer saw on sale in one country in eastern europe, production capacity has not made its marketing possible on a large scale.

Pavelle (USA)

A new colour paper, considerably improved, is now being manufactured, but it is not (for the time being) available in Europe. Production is at the moment fully taken up by some large stores in the USA. Material is made under licence from Ilford.

Tura (West Germany)

This dynamic small firm has now some colour materials on the market whose qualities are very competitive. *Turachrome 18* (50 ASA, 18DIN), miniature format reversal film, replaces *Turachrome 2*, of 15 DIN, which was based on the Kodachrome 1 principle. The Turachrome negative material (40 ASA, 17 DIN), and masked, is available in 35mm, 126 and Rapid cartridges as well as in 120. Processing is according to C-22.

Their colour paper CN111M is now also obtainable in rolls for automatic printers as well as in all the usual formats. Also their Color Photolinens, sensitised textiles for colour positives, which is a much appreciated speciality of Tura, continues to give enjoyment to many amateurs. Color-linen and CN111M are developed according to the Agfacolor procedure.

Optographis (USA)

We were surprised to see on the photokina stand of this exhibitor from Northbrook, Illinois, a range of products designed for colour reproduction by electrostatic means. The starting point of this process, *O/G Chroma* is a transparency which is projected through separation filters (red, green, blue), one after the other, on to an electrostatically-charged paper by means of an apparatus equipped with moveble eguide-lines serving as a masking easel. After each exposure, the paper is treated in a liquid which carries the appropriate pigment in a fine suspension. The print is dried, recharged electrostatically and the operations repeated. It is possible by the fourth exposure (in white light) to add a neutral black for the shadows. The total duration, about 15 minutes. The idea is an ingenious one and, practically, it can certainly be improved, since the prints that we inspected were rather disappointing and did not speak well for the process.

Conclusions

This review of photographic colour materials has included no special novelties which are likely to revolutionise colour photography. On the other hand, processes have been perfected and improved, and these are firmer steps towards the ideal. The classic processes are firmly maintaining their position. As regards negative/positive processes, automatic masking in the negatives is becoming more and more consolidated; in colour print papers, as a result of the appearance of the RC Type, a notable increase in productivity on the commercial scale has become possible. Turning to the silver-dye-bleach process, it is gaining ground slowly, but surely; and it now seems possible that the amateur too will be able to take advantage of it before very long.

E. Ch. GEHRET

MILESTONES IN TV AND LIGHTING
BY BAYNHAM HONRI

Who would have thought in 1924 that it would ever be possible to transmit by 'wireless', as it was then called, images of live people? Very few did. However, the telegraphy of still pictures by telephone lines or by radio was already an accomplished fact, starting, soon after the invention of telegraphy over lines, as a coding idea by Bain in 1842, but not becoming a really practical commercial proposition until about 1906, when, as usual, a number of inventors almost simultaneously evolved various ways of sending still photographic pictures by wire. These included Prof A. Korn (Germany), T. Thorn Baker (Britain), G. Fulton (USA), Edouard Belin (France) and others.

Stills by Telegraph
On 7 November 1907, Professor Korn received the first photograph from Paris at the *Daily Mirror* office, London, by special arrangement and with the co-operation of the GPO. It was a portrait of King Edward VII, transmitted and received by apparatus not unlike an Edison-Bell cylinder phonograph, scanning a picture of 50 lines per inch at the rate of two seconds per line. The cylinders of the transmitter and receiver had to be in synchronisation, of course, and the process took a long time. The scanning of the picture was vertical, because, as with Baird's first television attempts, upright close-up portraits were initially required. It was a slow process, requiring about 20 minutes or more to transmit a photograph and requiring a high standard of synchronisation to obtain intelligible results.

Newspapers Take a Hand
Special telephone lines were then rented jointly by the *Daily Mail* and the *Daily Mirror* between London and Manchester for newspaper use. To save time, pictures were sometimes sent divided into three separate parts, transmitted separately and joined together. Long shots were difficult and revealed differences which had to be made good by retouching. Specially-lit portraits with fully stressed 'modelling' gave the best results, flat pictures being difficult to transmit.

Contributions (inadvertent) by Criminals
From then on, progress was rapid, especially in USA where the Bell Telephone Laboratories (H.E. Ives and J.W. Horton) and the American Telephone and Telegraph Company (R.D. Parker and A.B. Clark) were in competition with the American General Electric Company (Messrs. Elster and Gertel). In 1911 a picture of a wanted criminal, transmitted by a Boston newspaper office to its New York affiliate, was handed to the police. This resulted in his immediate recognition and arrest on arrival at the railway station in New York. Naturally, this caught the attention of police all over the world, just as Dr Crippen was, apprehended on arrival in USA following a detailed Marconi wirelss telegraph message to the captain of the ship in

which he sailed from England.

Dramatic events of this type, revolutions, accidents and wars are the factors which impel technological progress, not the public exhortations of dedicated inventors like Eugene Lauste (photographic sound for cinema films), John Logie Baird (television), William Friese-Greene (kinematography) and Fox Talbot (negative-positive photography). Thomas A. Edison seemed to have had connections with each of these technological developments. It is unsafe and unrealistic to omit his name!

BBC progress
However, it was with the reproduction of still photographs that the BBC first attempted to broadcast visual images. This was from their original BBC HQ at 2 Savoy Hill, where the author was a youthful engineer in about 1924 and saw the 'Fultograph' cylinder machine in experimental use. At the same time, Capt Eckersley, BBC's Chief Engineer, had enquiries made of the activities of a compulsive young inventor down at Hastings, John Logie Baird. Baird knew about the scanning of still pictures with vertical lines and was also acquainted with the theory of the mechanically rotating Nipkow disc for dissecting a picture vertically and reproducing it mechanically. With the most preposterous Heath Robinson-like equipment, he did manage to achieve transmission by wire from room to room of more or less recognisable objects, of the simplest type. Baird attempted to scan an upright image of 30 vertical lines, at the rate of $12\frac{1}{2}$ complete pictures a second, the flying spot from the Nipkow disc being directed on to a selenium cell at the studio originating point. Mind your eyes, the flicker was ghastly! Powerful light was essential and when progress had been sufficiently satisfactory to try using the human face, the heat from the lamps, very close, was so great that a ventriloquist's dummy's head was used! The usual remote control of mouth and eyebrows gave the required movement.

Baird Makes Progress
A report to Capt Eckersley by Capt West (BBC Research) was guarded, but encouraging. John Baird brought his invention to London, was provided with accommodation and equipment by veteran Will Day, a cinema equipment specialist, and he set to work. By this time, many other inventors were in the field: C. Francis Jenkins (USA), Farnsworth (USA), Belin and Holweck (France), Alexanderson (USA), Goldsmith and Zworykin (USA), Karolus (Germany), Mihaly (Austria), Marconi research (Britain), Philips (Holland); competition was keen. Within a short time, Baird had made sufficient progress to attract more financial backing from the City and the very first television transmitting licence for a station with the call sign: '2 TV' was issued, for an installation and an aerial on the top floor of Motograph House, Upper St Martin's Lane, London, now

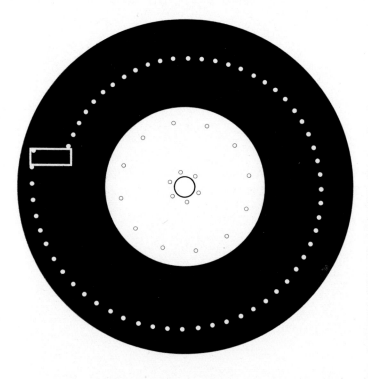

Above: Earliest method of scanning a picture, the Nipkow rotated disc.

Above Right: A first effort at a long shot on 30 line television.

Below: Left: A photographic still.
Right: Same still reproduced on 30 line Baird television system.

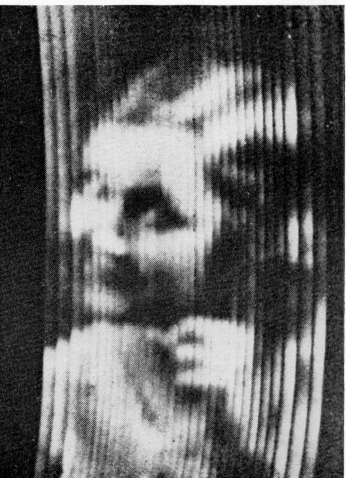

occupied by the Film Producers Guild. Later, Baird removed to larger premises in Long Acre, where the BBC became interested. When Broadcasting House, Langham Place, was built, BBC provided accommodation for a small television studio, for Baird to operate experimental transmissions. For some months the sound had to be transmitted before or after the picture, radiated from the 2LO transmitter and aerials on the roof of Selfridge's Department Store in Oxford Street. Later on, the picture was sent from the 2LO transmitter synchronously with sound from the long wave transmitter at Daventry Station 5XX. Of course, the transmissions from 2LO were made on the medium wave of 365 metres and 5XX was on 1600 metres—both quite unsuitable for television in these days.

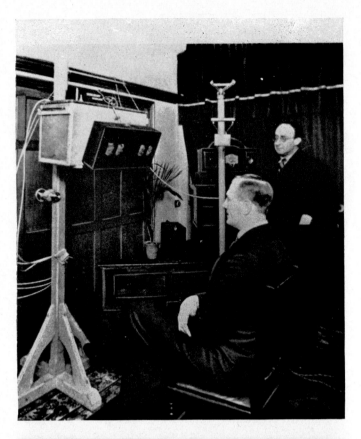

Foot-Candles Galore!

Owing to the enormous amount of light required with the Baird television system at that time, a flying-spot type of lighting system was introduced for scanning the scene, as shown in the illustration. The pictures were very crude, but they were living, reproduced at the then experimental 30 vertical lines per picture, $12\frac{1}{2}$ frames per second, and viewed with a magnifying lens through the revolving holes of a Nipkow disc, scanning a modulated neon lamp. It is fantastic that anyone should attempt to reassemble a picture from an image similarly dissected in this early Baird mechanical television camera—but somehow it worked. The reflections from the faces or subjects to be televised, illuminated by a rapidly moving spotlight, were picked up by a number of selenium cells. The Fernseh Company (Germany) evolved a somewhat similar system, and Mihaly (Austria) developed a narrow drum system for achieving the same prime objective of scanned spot-lighting. That was television lighting that was!

Why was there such a delay in turning over from low definition to high definition television? Capt A.G.D. West of the BBC gave the reasons:

(a) Early scanning methods in the studio did not give sufficient light to illuminate the scene well enough to be able to produce a useful television signal

(b) That the means of conveying television signals by lines, amplifier or radio carrier frequencies were not sufficiently good to transmit the requirements of high definition

(c) That no suitable means existed at that time for reproducing with accuracy any high definition picture.

The BBC summed-up by saying: 'Interesting! But it has no entertainment value!'

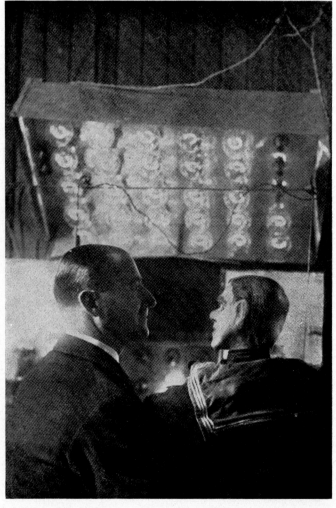

Increased Number of Lines

Immediate developments were firstly: the improvement of the 'spotlight' scanner with a much more intense spot covering 240 lines, instead of 30, by both the Baird Company in Britain and the Fernseh Company in Germany. This resulted in much better television lighting in the studio, though most peculiar make-up was required for actors' faces. Secondly, an intermediate cinema film system, on 16mm film, photographed the film, processed it within 30 seconds and fed it, still wet, through a television telecine play-off machine, complete with its photographic sound track. This enabled normal film studio lighting to be used. A third method of photographing a picture was an American electronic camera, the Farnsworth 'image dissector', which was a very early version of a wide range of non-mechanical electron television cameras.

From Low Definition to High Definition

In America a non-mechanical type of television camera

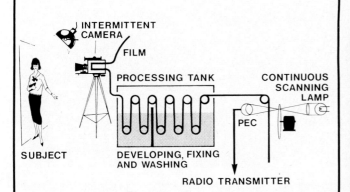

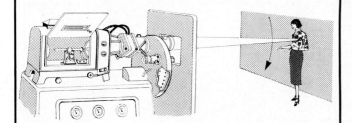

Above: Intermediate film process, used by Baird (UK) and Fernseh (Germany) in 1933-36.

Below: Intermediate film process in use in one of the BBC stages at Alexandra Palace in 1936.

Far Left Above: Flying spotlight scans the face of Bombardier Billy Wells at the Baird Long Acre Studio. Four selenium cells over the lens of the spotlight pick up the reflections.

Far Left Below: Huge banks of lighting were required for the first 30 line television, too hot for 'live' people. A ventriloquial dummy was used, with moving mouth, eyes and hair. Arthur Prince, a music hall star, brought his dummy along to the Baird studio and even appeared himself for a very short time!

Top: Peculiar make-up was required for flying-spot lighting. Blue lips and yellowish-white faces.

Above: The first stage lighting dimmer bank hand-operated at BBC's Alexandra Palace Studios, adapted from Strand Electric's 1928 'Grandmaster' stage lighting system. Rank-Strand Electric soon designed remote lighting consoles for controlling saturable reactor, tapped transformer and thyristor dimmers.

1950: Two television cameras used for putting pictures on to film for the cinema. The High Definition Films Limited's system at Highbury Studios.

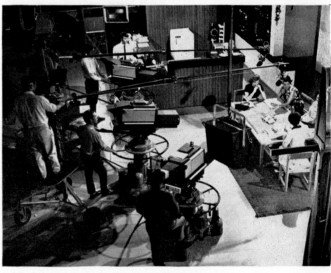

Above Left: Special Pye photicon television cameras in 1951 at the Highbury Studios of High Definition Films Limited using 800 lines *sequentially* scanned. The resultant high quality black and white picture was photographed on to 35mm film on a special Moy camera. The resultant picture was acceptable on a large cinema screen.

Above Centre Left: The Mole Richardson slotted lighting grid at the Marken Studios, Berlin, using telescopic suspensions for lamps.

Below Centre Left: A BBC lighting control room, fitted with a Strand Electric dimmer console with 3 rows pre-sets for individual or groups of lamps.

Below Left: Mole Richardson slotted lighting grid, for nionopoles or 'telescopes' for suspending lights. In the centre is one ventilation duct, silenced, of twelve which can be telescoped downwards. This grid was installed in the Pinewood new multi-purpose film-TV or videotape-stages at Pinewood, but similar grids are fitted at Southern Television, Yorkshire (Leeds), Westward (Plymouth) and elsewhere.

Top: A scene for colour television being videotaped at Southern Television's Southampton studios.

Above: Control Rooms (side by side) at Southern Television, Southampton. Foreground room: Thorn 4 File computer lighting console, with 150 'memories' of the best lighting results, designed at rehearsal. Middle room: Director, vision mixer and 'PA' in their control room. Far room: Sound control.

had been developed by Farnsworth, Zworykin RCA, Western Electric and others. After two years of experimental transmission of low definition pictures, BBC, like the American Broadcasting Corporation was seeking a higher definition system, which means that the picture must be scanned horizontally at 180 or more lines with a minimum number of 25 pictures per second. It was felt that, on this basis, a picture could be received of real entertainment value in the home in medium as well as close-up shots and even long shots. It was thought that such images must be of sufficient detail and flickerless to be watched comfortably for an hour or more! Furthermore, that the eye-straining effects of the primitive spotlight type of scanner in the television studio was disliked and incapable of being developed artistically. Line standards in various countries were rising, first to 120 and then to 180 upwards to 240 lines with 25 frames per second in England, 50 cycle mains supply, and 24 frames per second in USA, 60 cycle mains supply, all being called high definition.

The first television transmissions offered as a public service were made in London by the BBC with a transmitter from the Alexandra Palace in 1936. Two rival television systems were tested publicly: (a) Baird's system, with intermediate film camera, as described, at 25 frames per second and (b) a Marconi-EMI combined system of 405 lines, scanned 50 fields per second with interlaced lines, making up 25 complete frames per second and using the Zworykin Iconscope electronic camera, under licence from the RCA Company. Progress followed, from the RCA-Zworykin 'Iconscope' to the photoconductive Vidicon camera, to the same company's 3-inch Image Orthicon camera, the Pye Photicon, the Marconi Emitron, the Super Emitron, the EMI CPS Emitron. All of these cameras, in turn, improved in sensitivity and detail.

The intermediate film system was inclined to be temperamental. But announcers saying 'Goodnight, viewers!' at the end of a programme could rush round to see themselves 'on the air' half a minute later, as their images and voices were broadcast. The Marconi-EMI system was selected after only two or three weeks. Immediately war was declared British television ceased until after the war, when it was restarted with virtually the same equipment at the Alexandra Palace studios and transmitters.

Black and White Progress

The odd thing about the steady improvement in black-and-white television cameras from about 1950 until the advent of colour TV, is that, though camera sensitivity increased, there was no drastic reduction in the level of lighting in the studios. It was possible to obtain pictures with a lighting level of, say, 50ft candles but there were many other factors which had to be taken into account, such as the stopping down of lenses, for increasing the depth of focus, particularly with zoom lenses, the news hands off technique for reducing manual operational adjustments when 'on air' and of visual 'noise' on the picture—interference, graininess—when the level was raised.

The image Orthicon cameras of various British makes were generally used in both BBC and ITV studios and, on outside broadcasts, TV cameramen handled, focused, tracked and zoomed these large cameras with great skill on the dead-flat linoleum covered studio floors using the superb Vinten pedestals. But here again, stopping the lenses down a little more helped considerably. Also, running the tungsten lamps at about 2900°K could be coped with, whereas film studios demanded about 3200ft candles for black-and-white shooting. Colour temperatures were rigorously maintained for colour filming.

Lighting Controls

The first lighting controls in British television studios were at BBC's Alexandra Palace two stages, and comprised 36 hand-operated resistances (illustrated) made by Strand Electric. Before long that company, long-established in the live theatres but not in film studios, was able to provide a wide selection of different types of lighting dimmer controls. These could be pre-set in different manuals, rather like organ keyboards, complete with pedal operation, for fades and cross-overs. The manipulation of these fascinating lighting consoles was a joy to watch, if not to operate, because the ingenious precision had sometimes to be tempered with an artist's intuition, together with a hefty kick in the right place to rectify a fault! The consoles reverently controlled the voltages fed to the tungsten lamps by means of (a) mechanically and/or electrically-operated resistances (b) saturable reactor chokes (c) variable transformers (d) ratheon or electronic and latterly (e) thyristor carbon arcs, which are very rarely used in television stages, though there is a possible use for a compact light source lamp, such as the mercury-halide and Xenon units from Strand and Bell & Howell.

Further sophistication—nay, exotic—control of lights has been made possible by various memorising systems, which can record, amend, erase (and forget) the lighting plots designed by specialists with iron nerves and brilliant imaginations. To proceed further with the complications which have arisen with colour television developments would call for 30,000 more words. Automation and computerisation are with us already. Let us hope that the art of the engineer in this exciting field will not be prostituted by the 'creative' TV directors with too much psychedelia. The last word remains with photographic film, with special effects mixing cartoons with live pictures, travelling mattes high-speed camera work electronic aids, front projection, etc, etc. This can be seen in Disney's latest *Doorknobs and Broomsticks*, which should be seen from the technical angle as well as for sheer enjoyment.

The advent of colour has certainly changed the face of television. It is no longer mainly dependent upon key lights, Kicker lights, fill-lights and wanted (unwanted) shadows. It is based more than ever on colour temperatures, pictures and magnificent matching of camera outputs, telecine or even slides and film Chromakey and title in-lays. Too hard for anyone to remember, hence the computerised memory to remember levels is essential. From a start with no lighting grid at the BBC Alexandra Palace Studios to the sophisticated automated barrel systems at BBC's Television Centre, Shepherd's Bush, Southern Television's Mole-Richardson slotted grid system at Southampton, pantographs and automated remote controlled positioning of lanterns, progress has been fast, especially since colour arrived. But that is another story summed up in 'Fifty years of stage lighting' by an anonymous author published by Strand Electrical and Engineering Company Limited, in 1964. Its penultimate paragraph stated 'Today's dimmer controls use circuitry and manufacturing techniques beyond the imaginings of even 30 years ago. Yet, what we make today will seem just as crude technically and provoke in the future the same patronising smile as we tend to bestow on the work of our predecessors or even on work of our days. If on the other hand our predecessors were to turn up today, can we take it for granted that they would admire our solutions to problems they knew well enough?' These words could only have been written by Frederick Bentham, the philosopher of theatre and television lighting. They still hold good after all these years—and for evermore.

A History of Japanese Photography

In discussing a book entitled *The Past is Dead, The British Journal of Photography* editorially commented in the 4 September 1970 issue, 'In the course of little more than a decade, values which have long stood—including personal and aesthetic ones—seem to have been overthrown and an apparent anarchy set in motion.' By coincidence, that statement sounds like an appropriate description of Japanese photography's trends today.

A schism does exist between British photography in general and contemporary Japanese photography. The past —particularly Japan's consistent orientation towards British cultures—now appears nearly dead, even if small groups of Japanese photographers, mostly amateurs, still uphold the British style. The main current of Japanese photography is irrefutably led by 'those to whom the past is utterly dead'. As the *BJ* said, however, 'They are our inheritors—whether we like it or not—so we should try to understand them.'

The first camera imported to Japan in 1848 was a French-developed Daguerreotype, but the Japanese failed to produce any picture with it. The first Japanese-taken photograph was produced with a William Fox Talbot-developed system around 1853. The Talbot system withered soon, but the bridge thus established to link Japan with British photography was consistently consolidated by numerous leading workers, British and Japanese, in the several following decades.

Feudal Era

If cameras reached Japan only about a decade after they were invented in France and England, the development of Japanese photography was extremely slow in the 19th century, especially in the feudal era that lasted until 1867.

When the first Daguerreotype and Talbot cameras came, Japan was an agricultural country, lacking any modern chemical plants. Moreover violent political storms were sweeping a nation that was divided into scores of semi-independent feudal states each owned and ruled by a lord. They were loosely united by a military government run by hereditary *Shogun,* literally meaning: Generalissimo, in Tokyo, then called Yedo or Edo. The Emperor lived in Kyoto as a symbol of state, devoid of prerogatives or any political power. Shogun's autocratic power, however, was waning as the royalists were trying to restore the Emperor to a monarch's status. The whole economical and political climate was far from being favourable for the growth of photography.

Shogun's government adopted in 1639 an isolation policy, closing Japan's doors to all foreign nations, except only China and the Netherlands. Nagasaki in south-western Japan was the lone port opened to the traffic with the two countries. The first Daguerreotype was imported at Nagasaki by a well-to-do merchant named Toshinojo Uyeno in 1848. Although Uyeno was a highly educated intellectual, who was fluent in Dutch, he failed to form any images on silver plates. His sketch of the camera and notes remain.

Exactly when the Talbot camera and accessories came was not recorded. In 1925, the descendant of Lord Nariakira Shimazu, who ruled the southern province of Kagoshima, from 1848 to 1853, discovered 10 exposed negatives from a corner of the family treasure house. One of the negatives

A. Japan's oldest photograph—a Talbot type negative—taken by Lord of Shima *circa* of the Boys' Festival that's held 5 May every year.

B. Oldest Daguerreotype taken in Japan in 1854 by E.M. Brown, Jr., official Navy photographer, who came with Commodore Matthew Perry's fleet. Photo sho Kanzo Ishizuka, magistrate of Hakodate, with his three men.

C. Shimonoseki Battery occupied by the Allies—taken by Felix Beato in 1864. British vanguard platoon hoists the Union Jack (centre). Those concentrated arou Japanese guns are French sailors.

E   F

Nihon Bridge, Milestone Zero or where Japanese geographical mileage calculations start, in the centre of Tokyo in 1871 by Felix Beato.

Hikoma Uyeno, then a student at Nagasaki College of Chemistry, portrayed by mysterious Briton in 1858. This is the oldest wet plate remaining in Japan. Uyeno later became Japan's leading photographer.

Daughter of a viscount in traditional Japanese costume portrayed by Reiji Ezaki circa 1882. The girl was about 12 years old.

shows the May festival held in the Shimazu castle. Illustration A. Incidentally today's Japanese Empress Nagako hailed from this family. Other early photographs, preserved in Japan, were silver plates exposed and developed by foreign photographers who came with Commodore Matthew Perry's US Fleet and a Russian squadron in 1853, urging Japan to end its isolation policy, Illustration B.

Photographically more important were albumenised plate pictures taken by a British photographer, named Felix Beato, in the 1860s. He arrived in Yokohama in 1860 to join Charles Wirgman, a British Army veteran who came a year before as a correspondent of the *Illustrated London News*. The two Britons founded in 1861 the nation's first English-language journal *Japan Punch*. Another Briton, named John Black, took over management in 1870 and re-named the fortnightly as *Far East*. This journal operated until 1876 when Black moved to Shanghai. Beato left Japan a little earlier.

In 1864, Beato joined an allied squadron of British, Dutch, French and American warships, which hit back and briefly occupied a Japanese shore battery manned by xenophobic soldiers at Shimonoseki, Western Japan. Beato scooped the operation, which eventually changed the political course of the nation, by successfully taking action pictures—a marvellous feat considering all his handicaps and insufficient equipment, Illustration C.

Beato's secret was his special development method—guarded jealously as his trade secret—of the albumenised plate invented by Nièpce de Saint-Victor in 1839. When Beato used this plate in Egypt for the first time, he had to expose for three *hours*! His new development made him versatile enough to cover India's Sepoy Rebellion, 1857–59. Several of his pictures taken on this Indian assignment were exhibited at the photo-centennial exhibition held in 1939 in London. When he covered the allied operation in Japan, he exposed for three seconds, fantastically fast for then.

Beato made another scoop, which almost exploded into a Diplomatic *cause célèbre,* in 1867. He accompanied British Minister Harry S. Parkes when the latter submitted his credentials to Shogun, and snapped the Japanese leader. Shogun's adjutants refused to believe that any one could take a photograph so fast with available light, but turned purple in anger when they saw an advertisement a few days later in a Japanese newspaper. Beato offered to sell a print of Shogun's portrait at 1 *bu* 2 *shu*, roughly equivalent of 5 shillings 6 pence at the then value. Shogun's government immediately lodged a protest with the British Legation. Parkes expressed regret, but would not prevent Beato from selling the scoop picture to foreigners, if not Japanese.

A shrewd diplomat, Parkes had already written off Shogun's government, and was offering weapons and technical assistances to the royalists. France bet on the losing horse and urged Shogun to crush the 'rebels' with French aid. That situation may remind you of the Indian situation 100 years earlier when Lord Clive conquered a Bengal that was supported by France. The Indian débâcle was not repeated in Japan, mainly because Shogun declined the French offer and resigned in 1867, surrendering prerogatives and power to the Emperor. Japanese historians call this political change-over a 'Restoration' (of the Emperor's status), not revolution.

Beato continued to be active in turbulent Japan and his photographs were often inserted as supplements to the Yokohama journal. In 1871, he published a portfolio of 50 pictures entitled 'Photographic Views and Costumes in Japan', whose quality appeared many years ahead of his time, Illustration D.

Mysterious Briton

Beato, however, was a loner, who failed to associate with Japanese photographers or aspirants. His direct contribution to the growth of Japanese photography is rated low. One other British photographer, whose identity remains unknown, provided great help to a group of Japanese pioneers in photography.

Japan's first European-style college of chemistry was opened in 1857 at Nagasaki. Its Dean was a Dutch Navy medical officer named Pompe van Meerdervoort, who came to Japan with a wet plate camera and a photo manual book. Although he was evidently a beginner in photography, none of his pictures remain, van Meerdervoort included photography in the college curricula. In his first class was Ryojun Matsumoto, later the Japanese Army's surgeon-general, Hikoma Uyeno, son of the importer of the first Daguerreotype, and several other students, who were destined to become the nation's first leading photographers.

The students, hand-picked from many aspirants from all over the country, were brilliant and fluent in Dutch. They encountered no problems in learning the theory of photography. Their great unsolved problem was that the wet plate system was so difficult to handle that neither the professor nor students could produce any satisfactory pictures.

One day in 1858 Matsumoto saw a foreigner taking a picture with a camera similar to the professor's on a Nagasaki street. When Matsumoto befriended the photographer and confided the unsolved problem, the foreigner, who spoke Dutch but introduced himself as a Briton, cheerfully agreed to demonstrate his skill by taking portraits of Matsumoto and other students. The result delighted everybody, even the Dean, who humbly begged the Briton to visit his school whenever he could spare time and take over the photography course. The Briton, perhaps a businessman obliged and taught them all he knew. When he finally left for home a few months later, the British teacher donated to the school his camera and accessories along with a list of British exporters of photo materials, so that the college could replenish materials, Illustration E.

Pioneers

Hikoma Uyeno (1838–1904) opened his studio in Nagasaki in 1862, and several other students followed his example at other places. Uyeno continued to be active for many years, almost until the last day of his life, and trained many photographers. In the Tokyo–Yokohama area, two notable pioneers, who learned the trade from Americans, took up photography as their profession, but did not stick to it so long as Uyeno did. Gyokusen Ukai (1807–1888) operated his studio in Tokyo from 1859 to 1867, and Renjo Shimooka (1823–1914) in Yokohama from 1862 to 1876. Shimooka trained a number of pupils, but Ukai was a loner. Ukai closed down his studio, saying: 'The vicious superstition deeply rooted in the public regards photography as a "western witchcraft that absorbs the soul and spirit of those portrayed". This trade is unworthy for a man to pursue.'

For the rest of his life, he lived as a curio shop operator. In 1883, he buried all the wet plates he had in his family's graveyard, saying, 'I have sent all others to sitters, but cannot trace addresses of those in these plates. Rather than destroying them, I am burying them'. The graveyard was exhumed on the 30th September 1956 by a group of historians, who obtained consent from the late photographer's grandson. Unfortunately these historians were not scientific-minded, and failed to take appropriate precautions. About 40 plates were recovered, but practically all wrinkled and cracked as soon as they contacted air.

The supersition harassed other pioneers too. Uyeno later reminisced: 'Oldtimers dreaded the witchcraft so much that they would not dare walk the street near my studio.' Uyeno and other pioneers eked out a living mainly by portraying well-to-do intellectuals and foreigners, and also selling pictures of Japanese landscapes and dress abroad.

Uyeno's business took off at last in 1868 when 318 officers and men of a local army contingent swarmed to his studio each sitting before his camera. They were ordered to a perilous expedition to the north, and decided to leave their images with relatives. The windfall enabled Hikoma to pay back all debts that accumulated in the preceding six years.

Boom hit Uyeno's and other studios in the 1870s. Describing the situation in the period in an article contributed to an American magazine around 1890, W.K. Burton, a British professor at Tokyo University, wrote that Uyeno opened his business by importing a wet plate camera from France at $1500 and investing quite a lot on other equipment. The investments more than paid off in the 1870s because: 'Uyeno charged a modest $75 for a carte-sized glass positive ... reduced to $5 later. He was the only purveyor of photographic goods in the country and he must have made a pretty good thing of it—or someone must—to judge from the prices he charged. Here are a few of them. Nitrate of silver, $7.50 an ounce; collodion, $1 an ounce; sulphate of iron, $2 per pound, albumenised paper, $1 per sheet.' Readers should note that an American dollar in the 19th century was far more valuable than today's.

A qualified chemist, Uyeno ran small chemical plants, and virtually monopolised imports of photo materials, until a few traders entered this business in Yokohama and Tokyo. Among the pioneer traders was the Konishiroku Photo Company, founded in 1876, which now produces Konica cameras and Sakura films.

Uyeno pioneered not only in studio operation in Japan, but also in other phases of photography. He was appointed as the lone official photographer in 1877 when the southern Japanese revolted against the central government. This small counterpart of America's Civil War saw seven months of fierce actions. Uyeno, who joined the northern federal forces, moved around with his own platoon of two assistants and eight porters, who lugged his heavy 8×10 view cameras, many plates and darkroom equipment. All of his documentation of the war was done after the action had ended. When Japan fought the Manchu Dynasty of China in 1894–95, Uyeno covered the war again as a correspondent and again he failed to photograph war action. He was then indisputably Japan's top photographer, but his capability was more than 30 years behind Beato.

Japan's first war action pictures were taken by Uyeno's pupils and other correspondents in the Russo–Japanese War of 1904–5. All their action shots, however, were limited to ground operations. Not a single photograph was taken during the famed naval battle off Tsushima in 1905. These pictures illustrating history books are reproductions of oil paintings, Illustrations F and G.

Burton and Kajima

In the 1880s numerous new photographic studios mushroomed and flourished in various Japanese cities. If war documentation of the era was primitive, studio works preserved to this day still look fine, almost comparable in quality to those taken at today's studios. Either the pioneers were great, or posterity has stagnated, Illustration H.

One of the nation's foremost creative photographers who also runs a studio in Tokyo and who was one of the organisers of the 100 Years of Photography exhibition held in Tokyo in 1968, Miss Sue Imai: 'Think of the difference of fees before scorning us studio operators. Reiji Ezaki (1845–1910), for example, earned monthly an equivalent of today's £500. He did not work too hard, keeping enough time for experimental and creative activities. Alas! studios nowadays have to live hand-to-mouth. When virtually every Japanese family owns a camera, few will come and sit for us.' If studios charged a hefty price, prices of cameras and photo materials which were prohibitive, had to be completely imported. Only the wealthy and privileged could take up photography for a hobby.

Son of Tokyo's richest merchant, Seibei Kajima (1867–1924) visited Ezaki in 1885 asking for private lessons in photography 'for any amount of tuition'. Ezaki sent one of his assistants to Kajima's home every other day for one year-and-a-half. Upon graduation from this course, Kajima became a private student learning the scientific phase of photography from W.K. Burton, who had been teaching public sanitary engineering at Tokyo University since 1887 and who was an advanced photographer. That was the beginning of Burton's affiliation and guidance of the nation's fledgling photo community.

Born in 1853 at Edinburgh, Scotland as son of a historian, Burton made his headway fast both as public sanitary engineer and photographer. *The Cyclopaedia of Photography* edited by Bernard E. Jones credited Burton with remarkable achievements in the research of emulsions in 1880. *Le Dictionnaire Photographique* of France in 1956 introduced Burton as a man who made a significant research in the utilisation of selenium for coupling of shutter functions in 1881. Obviously Burton was many years ahead of Japan's leading photographers in the scientific phase. Burton later married a Japanese woman and lived in Tokyo until his death from illness in 1899. During his 12 years of stay, he authored numerous books on photography, and also a memorable portfolio entitled 'Japanese Costumes and Customs' that updated Beato's similar album.

Meanwhile Kajima spent money like water for photography after he headed in 1888 Tokyo's leading trading house. He told his managers to import any new camera, anything new and related to photography, at any price. Soon his company's warehouses went to the bursting point, then Kajima called in photographer friends, telling them, 'Help yourself to any item here.'

In 1889 Kajima organised the Japanese Photographers Society, making himself the treasurer general, Burton and Prof. Iwao Ishikawa at Tokyo College of Commerce as secretaries. In the inauguration ceremony, Burton delivered a lecture on platinotype, the newest type of photography at the time. Serving as his interpreter was Kazuma Ogawa, a US-educated professional who was rising fast as Tokyo's leading photographer. The Society was small, with only about 200 members, but it operated extravagantly. Kajima would reserve one full train and one full restaurant or hotel for their statutory meetings. At Kajima's request, Burton wrote to the London Salon, and succeeded to hold Japan's first large exhibition of many hundreds of British photographs in Tokyo in 1893. Kajima rented Tokyo's finest museum for one month to stage this exhibition. All the expenses came from the pocket of the treasurer general. Membership dues were nil.

In 1889, Kajima also established Japan's first factory of dry plates, installing Ogawa as President and Burton as Technical Superintendent. This project collapsed in 1891 under the snowballing deficits. This factory failed to produce hardly any plates that could be sold. In a report sent to Great Britain, Burton attributed the failure to Japan's lack of related chemical industries.

The Board of Directors at Kajima's company finally served him an ultimatum: 'Stop dissipation, or retire.' Kajima abdicated, married his long-time sweetheart Ponta, who was Tokyo's No. 1 Geisha, and launched a studio business in 1894. It went broke a year later, almost in synchronisation with the liquidation of his former business empire, Illustrations H and I. Epilogue: His Geisha wife refused to walk out on the washed out playboy, and supported him for 30 years until his death by teaching music and dancing to children. In 1963, a civil construction crew dug out from under the homestead, where Kajima once lived, a jar full of £70,000 worth of gold and silver. The government turned it over to a relative of Kajima now running a small chicken farm near Tokyo.

Kajima was a fairly good photographer. His pictures of *Kabuki*, another subject of his patronage, remain today as valuable documentary. After Kajima's downfall, another millionaire took over the patronage of the photo community. He was Toshimo Mitsumura (1877–1955) of Kobe. Although Mitsumura was more frugal than Kajima, he had to sell one of his modest-sized mansions in Tokyo to pay photographic bills. That mansion today is the US Embassy, Illustration J.

Photo Industry

Modernisation of Japan in the 19th century was spectacular with many new industries rising fast. An exception was the photo industry, that was non-essential in the eyes of the government. No matter how spendthrift, just two millionaires' resources could not be compared with the national budget which provided subsidies to 'key' industries.

Konishiroku began to produce dry plates in 1902, and

retreated quickly. The first Japanese dry plates were commercially made as late as 1919 by the Oriental Photographic Industry Co., which in 1971 produces only printing papers. The development of Japanese lenses and cameras was still slower. The first Japanese cameras, good enough for advanced amateurs, if not professionals, came out in 1935. They were 35mm range-finder *Canon,* equipped with *Nikkor* lens, produced by Nippon Kogaku, which waited 10 more years before manufacturing *Nikon.* The twin-lens reflex *Minolta* camera was also born in 1935. No one could deny that the initial Canon and Minolta were imitations, if not copies, of *Leica* and *Rolleiflex* cameras.

The sudden catapulting of Japanese lenses to fame after World War II owed much to the Japanese Navy's strong financial support of the research and development of binoculars and other optical instruments in the 1930s. It is generally agreed that the Japanese camera industry began to develop on its originality only from around 1960.

Photojournalism

Japanese literacy was quite high even in the feudal days and Japanese newspapers emerged in the 17th century, but the development of photojournalism was very slow. In November 1877, or a year after the British-operated *Far East* folded up, the first Japanese-language journal with photo supplements, *Shashin Zasshi* (Photography Magazine) was born. It lived until the third issue. Numerous similar ventures rose and fell as rapidly in the 19th century. The market was just too small, and advertisers did not exist. The first to stay alive for any time was *Shashin Geppo* (Photography Monthly), Konishiroku's public relations organ, which operated from 1894 to 1943.

The oldest established among today's Japanese pictorial magazines is *Fujin Gaho* (Women's Graphic), which started in 1903 as *The Japanese Graphic*. Its early issues contained more drawings than photographs. This magazine rode a boom when the Russo–Japanese War broke out in 1904, and sold 100,000 copies monthly. After the war boom ebbed, management converted it into a women's pictorial journal, Illustrations K, L, M and N. The nation's oldest magazine of photography is *Asahi Camera,* which was inaugurated by *Asahi Shimbun,* Japan's largest national daily newspaper, in 1926—72 years after the *BJ* started up. By the way, *Asahi Camera* is not related in any way with Asahi Optical Co, which was founded in 1919 for the production of spectacles. This company began to build the Asahi Pentax in 1957.

Asahi Camera monthly's birth followed the foundation in 1925 of *Asahi Camera Annual.* The first edition of this *Annual* listed 382 photo clubs, whose total members were estimated at less than 10,000. It carried 125 pictures selected from about 700 entries. Captions and the editorial as well as five articles contributed by leading authorities of the day were carried in Japanese and English. This tradition is upheld today. Unlike photographic annuals of other nations, *Asahi Camera Annual* continued to carry local products, although the editorial policy changed later. Since 1960, *Annual* editors began to select the best 100-odd items from millions of those made public in the preceding year, instead of soliciting clubs or photographers to contribute, Illustrations O and P.

G

H

J-1

G. Same girl in imported western costume portrayed by Reiji Ezaki *circa* 1

H. From W K. Burton's ''Japanese Costumes and Customs'' published *circa* 1
This is a scene of a Japanese maiden primping before the mirror.

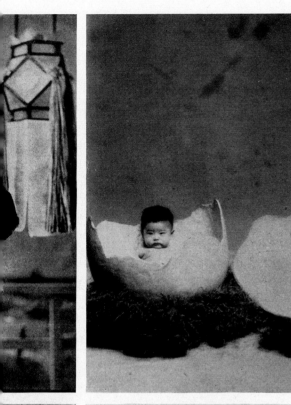

Geisha Ponta or Mrs. Seibei Kajima portrayed by Kazuma Ogawa *circa* 1889.
''Modernistic'' portrait of a baby by Seibei Kajima at his studio *circa* 1894.
2. Mamechiyo, Osaka's No. 1 Geisha, or Mrs. Toshimo Mitsumura, portrayed by her husband *circa* 1899.

Japan's counterpart of foreign countries' annuals, open for entries from many countries, is the *International Photo Salon of Japan* held annually by *Asahi Shimbun* since 1927. For the first edition of *Asahi Camera Annual*, the founding editor, Raycen Narusawa, stated: 'Art photography was born in Japan about 30 years ago, around 1895, but it was only recently that it reached the hands of common people . . . There may have been published several collections of photographic works by individual societies in the past, but unfortunately there was none that represents photographic work of the whole of Japan. In England, there is an annual entitled *Photograms of the Year* which has now reached its thirtieth edition, and in America the *American Annual of Photography*, now in its thirty-ninth year. Japan's similar publication should have appeared a long time ago. . . Art photography is still in its infancy throughout the world. Spiritually, technically, it must go through all kinds of trials and hardships, particularly in Japan, and it requires a length of time to make a foreign art that of one's own. From imitation to self-awakening, to anguish, to emancipation, then the originality; thus bringing a work, one's own, expression.'

The 1925 edition sold at 2.50 yen. In terms of relative purchasing power, 2.50 yen of 1925 was far more valuable to postwar devalued 1700 yen or £2, the price of the 1970 edition. The 1925 edition had to be priced high, because the book contained only two pages of advertisements by importers, playing up Ilford's Screened Chromatic Plates, yellow label 270 and blue label 400. Japan's own photo industry was not yet in good enough shape to run an advertisement.

In the founding editorial, Narusawa also noted: 'Photography in Japan is placed in a most unfavourable condition, owing to the fact that the whole of photographic materials are imported. There is a heavy duty, and the loss through the existing rate of exchange, all sends up the price of photographic materials.' Illustrations Q and R. Narusawa was more gloomy when he wrote an editorial for the inaugural issue of *Asahi Camera* magazine in April 1926: 'The progress of amateur photography was greatly retarded by the heavy import duty, which amounts to as much as 100%, *ad valorem,* on films and cameras, and only a bit less on other photographic materials. Consequently the Japanese photography is now stagnant, and the publishing business hit by depression. If a photography magazine, meant for a limited section of the community, is launched at this time, we must be prepared for very rough sailing ahead. But a baby cannot choose its time of birth. Once it is born in the worst circumstances, we must do everything to help it grow. Behind the dark clouds, however, not too far away is the dawn of a new era.'

Just as foreseen by Narusawa, who functioned earlier as *Asahi Shimbun*'s correspondent in American and Great Britain, very rough sailing beset *Asahi Camera Annual* and magazine. Moreover the military grounded (or rather torpedoed) them for a forced hibernation that lasted until 1949. Narusawa, however, was lucky enough to live until 1962 when he died at 85, after seeing his baby magazine's circulation rise to 150,000 equalling the combined total of all other Japanese photo magazines.

Also extremely slow was the growth of newspaper photography. Japan's first daily that adopted the half-tone process for reproduction of photographs was *Mainichi Shimbun,* whose 1 July 1890 issue carried, for the first time, 'mug'-shots of 16 new members of Parliament. It was only after 1912, when *Asahi Shimbun*'s two technicians invented a new method of obtaining matrix direct from copper plates, that many Japanese newspapers began to illustrate news stories with photographs.

British photojournalist Herbert Ponting operated in and about Japan for five years from 1901, and produced many excellent photographs. Unlike Burton, however, Ponting did not associate with Japanese photographers or make available his work to Japanese publications. Like Beato, Ponting failed to influence the Japanese.

Pictorialism

Almost throughout the 19th century, the Japanese were satisfied when their photographs were sharply focused and the compositions 'well-balanced'. Japan began to import pictorial photography from Great Britain and Europe from around the turn of the century. Champion for the new school was Tetsusuke Akiyama (1880–1944), a well-to-do Tokyo dilettante, who introduced gum-bromide, bromoil and other pictorial methods, and then established in 1907 *Tokyo Shashin Kenkyukai* (Tokyo Photo Study Group). This group gradually gained hegemony, and lorded over the Japanese photo community in the 1910s.

Akiyama wrote for *Asahi Camera Annual* in 1925: 'Unquestionably Japanese photographers have received strong stimulus and influence in the past two decades from the Royal Photographic Society of Great Britain, London Photographic Salon, Photograms of the Year, and Amateur Photographer & News.' By referring to 'the past two decades', Akiyama meant the Anglo–Japanese Alliance that lasted from 1902 to 1921. Akiyama also named the following photographers as his favourites: Great Britain's H.J. Mortimer, Alexander Keighley, Carine Cadby, E.O. Hoppé, J.M. Whitehead and A.L. Coburn; Germany's Rudolf Duehrkoop, Nicola Perscheid, Albert Meyer and Otto Ehrfardt; Belgium's Leonard Misonne, and France's Robert Demachy and C. Puyo. Of these photographers, well remembered by Japanese photographers in general were Hoppé, whose exhibitions were held by *Asahi Shimbun* in Tokyo and Osaka in 1923, and Coburn, whose pictures illustrate all Japanese books of photo history. Akiyama's predominance began to wane after a new powerful leader, named Shinzo Fukuhara (1883–1948), emerged.

Also son of a well-off Tokyo family, Fukuhara studied chemistry in America from 1908 to 1912, then toured all over Europe for one year before coming home in 1913 to head his family business of pharmacy. In London, he visited Marion and Co and was told, 'A Soho Reflex of your requirement must be custom-made, and cannot be delivered soon.' Fukuhara made full payment in advance, and waited six months until the $2\frac{1}{2} \times 3\frac{1}{2}$in format camera, evidently of the tropical version costing 50% more than ordinary ones, reached him in Paris. The young Japanese fell in love with the British camera at once, and quickly exposed some 2000 plates with the camera and a 13in lens, mostly in Paris. Although he studied bromoil with Rudolf Duerkoop at

K1

K2

L

K-1. Tokyo cityscape: Mitsui & Co. headquarters near Nihon Bridge in 1895 ta[...] by Kazuma Ogawa.

K-2. Tokyo cityscape: Downtown near Uyeno Park in 1895 taken by Kazuma Og[...]

L. A Japanese Army platoon sniping a fleeing Russian contingent in the Battl[...] Port Arthur in 1904, from 15 January 1905 issue of the Japanese Graphic.

M. German Prince Carl Anton visits Japanese Army sub-area headquarters at D[...] Manchuria. From 15 April 1905 issue of the Japanese Graphic.

On behalf of King Edward, Prince Arthur of Connaught visited Japan in February
06 to bestow the Order of Garter to Emperor Meiji. Photo shows the Prince with
s suite and Japanese reception committee. The Prince seated beside Admiral
H. Togo in front row.

Rare snapshot carried by the 1 March 1906 issue of the Japanese Graphic.
arquis Hirobumi Ito, who studied in England in his young days, and Marchioness
(facing this way in the centre), who was formerly a *Geisha*. Photo taken at a
garden party held 1 February 1906 in Seoul, Korea.

Hamburg, he lost interest in the method and switched to his own style, following the French impressionism. His pictures made public soon after his repatriation kicked up a sensation at once, for they were so fresh and new to the Japanese. Fukuhara married a Geisha, organised the Japan Photographic Society, and continued to spend a lot of money on photography throughout his life. But he was not another Kajima. Completely satisfied with Soho Reflex, Fukuhara showed no interest in any other cameras. Furthermore, Fukuhara was also a great businessman, who successfully built his drug store, Shiseido, into Japan's largest and one of the world's biggest cosmetic companies.

Asahi Camera's founding editor, Narusawa, sought and obtained full support of Akiyama and Fukuhara in the nursing of his prematurely born babies, and took pains to carry pictures belonging to the two opposing groups as well as smaller provincial clubs. But Narusawa would not hide his critical view of the pictorialism, which he knew was already outmoded in Europe, if not in England. In the inaugural editorial, he stated: 'Looking through all the work that has been selected, most of them are landscapes which are more or less expressed in delicate line and tone and lack grandeur and strength ... Some are on level with those of European artists, but, on the whole, the standard is much lower than that of our European friends.'

Shortly after his monthly magazine was launched, Narusawa energetically stumped the nation, and succeeded in the amalgamation of more than 200 amateur clubs into the All-Japan Photographic Federation in 1926. The Federation's enunciated objective was to establish 'universality of photography', and its unspoken mission was to obliterate the residual feudalism of Japanese to follow powerful individual leaders worshipfully. This Federation today functions as Japan's most powerful amateur group, although its membership of 30,000 is smaller than commercially-sponsored *Olympus Camera Club*'s 90,000 and *Nikkor Club*'s 80,000. Akiyama's and Fukuhara's groups also continue to operate in 1971, each with about 300 pictorialist members.

A new wave was brought to pre-war Japanese pictorial scenes by Iwata Nakayama (1895–1949). Hailing from one of Kobe's richest families, Nakayama chose photography as his profession. After graduating from Tokyo Academy of Fine Arts, he studied photography in the United States from 1918 to 1926, then conducted an extensive study tour of Great Britain and Europe for a year. Nakayama rose to fame in 1929 by winning the first International Commerical Photo Contest conducted by *Asahi Shimbun*. He followed it up with a steady stream of abstract, surrealistic and modernistic pictorialism—shocker and eye-opener to many Japanese. In 1932 Nakayama established in Tokyo a new photo monthly magazine *Koga* (Light Picture)—a movement comparable to the formation of the Linked Ring in London in 1892. Nakayama selected the following partners: Kozo Nojima (1889–1914), operator of Tokyo's leading photo studio, who broke off from Fukuhara's Society; Ihei Kimura, the nation's first Leica photographer, and the leading photo critic, Nobuo Ina, MD; both Kimura and Ina are vigorously active in 1971, Illustrations S and T.

Koga crusaded against, among others, the taboo on nude

photography. This must sound incredible if you know about today's deluge of naked women in Japanese publications, stage, TV and movie, and if you remember that mixed baths were not tolerated in many Japanese provinces until the 1930s.

In fact it was scandalous for many years for Japanese women to show their legs in the public, although bare breasts were less offensive. When a leading Japanese artist came back from France and exhibited a nude painting in 1895, police intervened and draped a part of the picture. Japanese sexual postcards, which were fashionable around 1900, were all costumed, like samples reproduced here, none like European 'Pin Up 1900' as shown at *photokina* of 1970, Illustrations U, V and W.

Japan did have a strong tradition of nude art in the wood-block arts of the feudal age. But *the past was dead* for the Japanese who were too busy to study European aesthetics. *La Beauté Plastique,* a French manual of nude art published around 1900, that was avidly studied by the Japanese, declared: 'Oriental women are of a peculiar type, with heavy joints, the bulging lips, the black eyes; their aesthetics in general lacking charm. Chateaubriand said that one must look at them from afar, so that their details do not show.' The categorical statement found an echo in a British portfolio of nude photographs published in 1955. An introduction to *Oriental Model* by John Everard, published by Robert Hale Limited, London, stated: 'In Japan . . . the majority of both sexes have elongated trunks and abbreviated legs almost to the point of distortion by western standards.'

Perhaps such a European concept was partly responsible for the reluctance of Japanese women for a long time to pose in the nude. Japanese pioneers in nude photography soft-focused to blur details, and cropped or 'elongated the abbreviated legs' in the darkroom process. Nakayama's and Nojima's nudes caried by *Koga* were more clearly delineated. By today's definition, however, Nojima's were semi-nudes. Nakayama included cropped nudes as 'objects' in sur-realistic compositions. Even so, their works shocked and infuriated many a moralist. Nude photography in full meaning emerged in Japan only after women were fully emancipated and their physiques improved.

More successful was Kimura's pioneering in 35mm photography. His success was especially significant because Kimura was the first leading photographer who was born and bred by a middle class family. After finishing commercial high school in Tokyo, he worked for three years at a sugar distributor in Taiwan, where he befriended a small studio operator and observed his operation from time to time. After returning to Tokyo, he started up a small studio in 1924 and went broke four years later. In 1929, a Zeppelin visited Japan and its captain demonstrated a Leica. Kimura saw in the new camera a widened horizon, sold all his studio equipment and borrowed as much as he could to buy one of the first Leicas that reached the Japanese market. His early work with the Leica—mostly portraits of intellectuals taken unposed with available light—greatly impressed Nakayama, who immediately asked Kimura to join him in the new avant garde sect.

Kumira continued to rise. His first solo exhibition of Leica photography in 1934 created a sensation, greater than that

P. A British squadron of five warships commanded by Admiral Noel made a go will visit of Japan in October 1905. Photo shows snapshots of British sailors a welcome party in Hibiya Park by the Municipality of Tokyo. From 31 October 1 issue of the Japanese Graphic.

Q-1. ''Portrait'' by Tanetada Konishi of Tokyo from the 1925 Asahi Camera Ann

"The Girl" by Seiya Umbe of Nagoya from the 1925 Asahi Camera Annual.

Village Lads" by Ugetsu Tanaka of Osaka from the 1925 Asahi Camera Annual.

S. Seine River taken by Shinzo Fukuhara in 1913.

T. Suchow, China taken by Shinzo Fukuhara in 1934.

caused by Fukuhara's more than a decade earlier. Two of Kimura's early pictures were carried by the 1934/35 edition of Great Britain's *Photography Annual.* In 1938 America's *Life* magazine used Kimura's portrait of a Japanese prime minister for cover. That was the first Japanese-taken cover used by the American magazine. However, *Koga* continued to lose money. When Nakayama and Nojima paid off the nineteenth month's deficit, their resources hit the bottom. *Koga* was closed down, Nakayama became ill, and Nojima retreated to his studio.

The new era as envisaged by Narusawa in 1926 was very slow to arrive.

Wartime Stagnation

The so-called Manchurian Incident erupted in 1931, and escalated to total war against China in 1937, then further to the Pacific War 1941–45. The tripartite pact with Nazi Germany and Mussolini's Italy was concluded in 1936. As the war intensified, the military tightened control of everything. Free expression was no longer practicable, and Japanese aspirations towards creative photography stagnated.

In the days of the Anglo-Japanese Alliance, Japan received a strong influence from Great Britain, not only in the military and industrial phase, but also in the cultural, especially in photography. But the German and Italian influence on Japanese photography in the warring decade of 1936–45 was negligible.

Asahi Camera, in October 1937, published the *World's Photographic Masterpieces,* a collection of 275 photographs selected from 2923 entries from 36 nations to the year's *International Photo Salon of Japan.* Perhaps that was the last pre-war book of photography retaining some 'free expression', although Japanese *avant garde* photographers like Nakayama, Nojima and Kimura turned their backs on the *Salon.* A critique by chief judge Shinzo Fukuhara in the book intrigues posterity, for it reflected the Japanese salonists' way of thinking at the time. Fukuhara wrote in part: 'Because space does not permit me to comment on each individual work, I should like to discuss briefly trends of various countries. British photography reflects its extremely long tradition. British people are noted for their stalwart characteristics and conservatism in photography. I was heartened to recognise their unwavering academic approach . . . Germany is a country of science. Its photography is backed up by time-honoured technological tradition. German photography asserts their will to solve everything scientifically. Italy is rather isolated from other photo-minded nations, and its climate is milder. I found the impressionistic and symbolic trend of Italian photography somewhat resembling the Japanese trend. US photography in general is cheerful and easy. It is neither academic nor sensitive. American photographs lack depth, but are delightfully buoyant'.

In 1942 the military branded *Asahi Camera* as 'nonessential and unworthy of expending paper and ink' and forced it to be suspended. *Asahi Camera Annual* 1942, published in July 1942, was one of the last wartime publications of photography. Most pictures in this book are poor, definitely inferior in quality to the 1937 book or even the inaugural *Annual* of 1925. One work each of Fukuhara and

Nakayama carried by the 1942 portfolio show them in uninspired, stale mannerism. More interesting was an appendix article written by Shigene Kanamaru, who became dean of *Nihon University*'s photography school after the war. Kanamaru appealed to the military not to destroy art photography, saying: 'When the nation fights for its survival, certain people insist that photographic art must be sacrificed. That is not a mere opinion. Recent developments indicate that photography for art's sake is being smothered . . . I, however, do hope that photographic art must not die, but develop, in this war . . . I mean a photographic art of new concept, not like the past pictorialism that was not much more than a pastime. New photographic art must carry the spontaneous and determined will of photographers'.

Photography was doomed in Japan during the war of attrition, even without the military pressure. Cameras and photographic equipment became increasingly expensive as imports shrank. The war-time security dictated 'fortified zones', where picture-taking was forbidden. As the Allied blockade began to take effect, supplies of cameras and materials became very scarce from early 1944, and only professionals for 'essential' assignments received very low rations.

Women's Activities

The history of Japanese photography lacks any great female photographers comparable in calibre to Julia Margaret Cameron or Margaret Bourke-White. For many years indeed, photography was a man's profession or hobby in Japan. The Restoration of 1867 did usher in a partial emancipation of women along with the national modernisation. Certain Japanese ladies achieved as much as the greatest men in the 19th and 20th Century—but not in photography.

Not a single woman's work was placed in *Asahi Camera Annual* 1925. The *Ladies Camera Club,* Japan's first such organisation, was founded in Tokyo in 1937. None of the Club's entries were accepted by the year's Salon. The 1942 *Annual* contained only one Japanese housewife's contribution. After World War II, Japanese women obtained suffrage and their emancipation expanded its scope. From about 1960 photography became accessible to any Japanese, men, women and children alike. Nevertheless only a handful of professional women photographers like Miss Imai are ranked high today. The 1970 *Annual* opened space to only two ladies' works.

Being widely questioned now is just how long men's supremacy in Japanese photography will last. When two young photographers of the nude, who are men, Kishin Shinoyama and Yoshihiro Tatsuki, held solo exhibitions last year, each drew some 100,000 admirers in a week. About one half of them were young girls. Whenever the photographers appeared at the galleries, female fans mobbed them, asking for autographs or offering to pose for them in the nude. The past is dead!

Postwar Upheavals

Japan's surrender to the Allies in 1945 and the subsequent occupation by the Americans until 1952—unprecedented in Japanese history—brought about upheavals—political, social, moral, aesthetic and every other aspect—far more

U2

U1

U3

U-1. Japanese Pin-up 1900: A posing Geisha.

U-2. Japanese Pin-up 1900: A Geisha entering the bed by lifting the mosquito

U-3. Japanese Pin-up 1900: Seven leading Geisha of Niigata.

violent than those stemming from the Restoration of 1867.

Values which have long stood were thrown to the winds. Pictorial photography was no exception. The Torpor and anarchy that had prevailed for awhile were soon replaced by a series of drastic reforms carried out by the American occupation. The wealthy, deprived of titles and privileges, and landlords, whose estates were expropriated in the agrarian reform, sold expensive cameras and others to eke out living. Common people barely subsisted—with no time or money for hobby.

A widely-accepted theory holds that Japan was 'Americanised' very quickly and thoroughly, because the American culture filled the Japanese mental vacuum. It must be pointed out, however, that many Japanese vomitted the American culture soon afterwards as rapidly as they swallowed it.

Asahi Camera resumed publication in October 1949, when Japan appeared to be nearly back on its own feet economically. Culturally the postwar anarchy was winding up, just as the US military's precensorship of Japanese publications was ending. *Asahi*'s postwar editor Hideo Tsumura recruited the services of Ihei Kimura and Nobuo Ina, avant garde leaders, in re-establishing the art photography in Japan.

If the US occupation's influence on Japanese photography was skin-deep, almost unfathomable was the influence wielded by America's topflight photographers who began to visit Japan from around 1950, associated with Japanese photographers and made available their works to *Asahi Camera* and other Japanese publications. Those American photographers included Margaret Bourke-White, Eugene Smith and just too many others to be listed here. Japanese photojournalism and commercial photography especially owed greatly to impetus and stimulus given by the Americans. In other phases of photography, Japanese learned a lot from leading French masters like Henri Cartier-Bresson, Robert Doisneau, and Brassai, as well as Swiss photographers like Emil Schultess and Werner Bischof, and South Africa's Sam Haskins, who now lives in London.

Practically all of the important photo exhibitions held in postwar Japan were of US photography. Hardly any came from the United Kingdom. When the British Week was observed very successfully for one month in Tokyo in 1969, a few British photographic exhibitions were held. They were so poor or incongruous that they disappointed even the most ardent Anglophiles. From about 1960, younger generation Japanese photographers, not scarred mentally by the war or not moulded by pre-war pictorialism, began to assert their originality. This new trend has been sometimes misinterpreted as de-Americanisation. Fukuhara once defined his concept of photography as 'harmony of lights' and likened the amateurism to the traditional Japanese habit of composing *Haiku,* the 17-syllable Japanese poetry. Fukuhara's subjects were often dwarfed trees and miniature gardens. A great businessman, Fukuhara as a photographer elected to 'think little' like most other Japanese photographers before World War II. Nowadays, young Japanese professionals 'think big' attitude seems to reflect the overall trend—if not exactly the Zeitgeist of Japan.

剏 生 · 中山岩太 · 東京　V

濁河靜波 · 井上武夫 · 滿洲

W

V. ''Genesis'' by Iwata Nakayama from the 1942 Asahi Camera Annual.

''Sungari River, Manchuria'' by Takeo Inouye from the 1942 Asahi Camera Annual.

CINE RETROSPECT OF THE YEAR

BY PETER A WEST

FILM PRODUCTION

The trend towards shooting films on location continued throughout the year. According to a paper read at the 'Film '71' Film Technology Conference, a recent survey showed that 90% of pictures made in the USA for cinema release were being shot on location. The percentage was lower in film series made for television, but here too a considerable number were being shot on location throughout the world. The same survey showed that in features the camera was rolling for only 1 minute out of 38 minutes spent on a production (in TV series 1 out of 27 minutes), and that the director used only 25% of the time spent on a set—the rest being taken by the crew and technicians in setting up and preparing equipment.

In these circumstances it is not surprising that new, lighter equipment was being developed and put into use in an effort to reduce waiting time and costs. In particular, lighter cameras that can reduce set-up time, specially on difficult locations where manhandling over rough ground may be necessary, were introduced; they also offer considerable savings in transport costs when moving by air. Frequently, other features were included designed to save time and reduce costs.

35mm CAMERAS & ACCESSORIES

Thus the new Panavision R200 camera is 18kg lighter than other similar production cameras, and its 200 degree shutter allows lighting to be reduced by about one sixth for a given lens aperture. Height and bulk can be further reduced by fitting a 120m/400ft magazine and blimp cover, while the crystal-controlled motor works off relatively lightweight batteries.

But even so, this camera is far removed from the sort of portability that people have become used to when working in 16mm for television, namely a camera that is relatively silent in operation and can be hand-held when the occasion demands—such as for shooting inside moving vehicles, or 'walkie-tracks'. Two new cameras have attempted to give similar flexibility to 35mm film users: The Panavision hand-held camera is a converted Arriflex IIc, fitted with a long coupling piece which places the magazine behind the operator's shoulder. A single, robust lens-mount replaces the turret and adds rigidity to maintain correct lens to film register. The whole unit is housed in a lightweight blimp which cuts down noise sufficiently to allow direct sound shooting in many outdoor locations. However, the camera is rather heavy and clumsy, and too noisy for sync shooting in many circumstances.

The other new introduction, so far seen only in prototype, is the Arriflex 35BL. This is a completely new construction, using a newly-designed register-pin movement, and like its 16mm predecessor is designed to be inherently silent in operation, with the drive and take-up mechanisms mounted on rubber to isolate them from the housing. With a normal lens mounted in the single lens-mount, the noise level at 1m in front of the camera is 39db; this can be reduced by 4–6db by surrounding the lens with a small blimp. This should make the camera quiet enough for most location shooting. For use on a sound stage it can be enclosed in a studio-type blimp, which cuts the noise level down to 21db—as good as most studio cameras, though it must be admitted that the 35BL lacks some of the refinements expected of a full studio camera, such as variable shutter for coping with unavoidable changes of light-level on some scenes, magnifier and filters in viewfinder etc. But then the camera is not basically designed for that type of work but rather for use on location. Although it weighs 20lb, the camera balances well on the shoulder, with the reflex finder eyepiece falling naturally at the operator's eye. Drive is from a printed-circuit dc motor with electronic control for running at 24 or 25pps, with a choice of 50 or 60Hz pilot-tone output for synchronising, and an optional accessory for crystal speed control to give wire-less sync when utmost portability is required.

Accessories were also introduced to make the 35mm Arriflex—essentially a hand-camera—better suited to feature production requirements. ATC of Rome produced an improved Professional viewfinder, incorporating variable magnification and colour and b&w viewing filters, which put the operator's eye 4in further back than usual so that the head clears the magazine and either eye can be used for viewing, as well as a flat motor base and several follow-focus attachments that allow precision focus-pulling by the camera assistant from beside the camera.

LENSES FOR 35mm

New, faster, high-quality lenses were introduced, which can reduce lighting requirements, and in particular allow shooting location interiors with the minimum of added light. Angènieux produced a 50mm f/0·95 lens, though the construction was such that it did not allow sufficient rear clearance for mounting on reflex viewfinding cameras; this makes accurate focusing difficult with the very small depths of field involved. Panavision introduced a new set of super-speed, high quality lenses for non-anamorphic photography, which are 1 to 2 stops faster than the nearest equivalent modern lenses for studio reflex cameras. The fastest in the series is a 55mm T1·1, and others include a 28mm T1·9, 35mm T1·3, and 127 and 150mm T1·7, all to fit the R200 or PVSR reflex cameras.

It has long been recognised that zoom lenses can give extra flexibility and reduce set-up times. However, until recently, penalties had to be paid in things like minimum focusing distance and width of taking angle available, in rotation of the front cell making the fitting of matte-boxes and some filters difficult, and in general the image quality not being up to the best produced by fixed focal length lenses. During the year new designs appeared which to a large extent have eliminated most of these shortcomings. Most of these have been computed with the requirements of film production in mind, and are not just re-scalings of television designs. The newcomers include the Angènieux 20–120mm T3, which gives a usefully wide angle and focuses down to under 1m; the Canon 25–120mm T2·8 K35 Macro Zoom, which focuses in the normal manner down to 1·2m and then allows focusing right down to 5cm from front lens surface by the displacement of an internal lens element—although the lens cannot be zoomed in this macro range, simple and effective focus shifts are made possible by operating the auxiliary focusing lever; and the RTH proto-type 20–100mm T3·2 Cooke Varotal, which uses a new zoom principle allowing the overall size to be reduced and the front lens element to be held stationary for focusing (down to 0·7m from the film plane)—in addition the rear lens element can be changed to give longer focal lengths (at reduced maximum aperture) for exterior shooting.

Occasionally there is also a call for really long-range zooms. Angènieux have produced a new version of their 25–250mm lens for BNC and similar studio cameras, and Samuelson's have modified one of these to give a 20:1 continuous zoom range—25–500mm T9·5, which was used most effectively for the final shot of '10 Rillington Place'.

Developments have taken place in servo controls of zoom lenses. Designs in which the zoom rate can be varied at the turn of a knob have become quite common, but a new introduction is a zoom servo controlled by a small, hand-held computer in which the zoom *time* can be pre-set over any selected focal length limits of the lens, and varied smoothly between 0·5 and 99sec; this time remains constant even when the zoom or magnification range is altered, which can be done remotely from the hand control unit. In addition, this allows 'soft' starts and finishes to the zoom movement, the amount of damping applied at each end being separately adjustable by turning the appropriate control knobs. The unit, by Discovery Technology Corporation and handled here by Cintron, seems to offer far greater flexibility and repeatability than other servo systems.

Panavision have made a special adaptation of the 20–120-mm T3 Angènieux zoom for their studio cameras, and this can be fitted with a totally silent zoom servo using magnetic drive in place of the usual gears.

CRYSTAL MOTORS

When cameras are used on a sound stage, it is usual to power them from a 3-phase mains supply, and this is also used either to drive a synchronous magnetic film recorder, or (these days) to supply a pilot-tone signal for recording on ¼in tape alongside the audio signal, which maintains sync in the subsequent transfer to magnetic film. On location it has usually been necessary to power studio cameras from locally generated 3-phase, or to change the motor for a multi-duty type that could be operated from batteries; as these motors usually operated at 96 volts, and, with their governor controls, were relatively inefficient, large batteries were necessary. During the last year or so highly efficient constant speed crystal-controlled motors have come into use, which need a very small battery supply only. They are available from Cinema Product Developments, Panavision and Perfectone for Mitchell BNC, NC, or derived cameras, and the former also offers crystal-controlled motors for the S35R MkII and Arri 35 IIc cameras. Besides the reduced power consumption, sync shooting (with several cameras at once, if desired) without interconnecting cables is possible by fitting a matched crystal oscillator to the tape recorder to provide the pilot-tone track.

SOUND

In an attempt to simplify sound pick-up on location, and minimise the inconvenience caused by microphone booms, radio microphones concealed in the actors' clothing have been used occasionally. At times these have not proved entirely successful, due to fading and interference at the VHF frequencies employed. In an attempt to overcome this, Cintron have introduced UHF radio microphones, but there is not, to date, sufficient experience to say whether this will overcome the problems. An alternative approach has been developed by Kudelski, whose Nagra SN miniature tape recorder is small and light enough (147×100×26mm, 0·57kg) to be worn by artists as a personal recorder. The machine uses 3·81mm (0·15in) wide tape running at 3¾ips, and gives results up to full professional standards; a sophisticated automatic level control is built in, but manual gain control is possible with an accessory unit. Another accessory allows crystal-generated pilot-tone, divided down to 10Hz, to be recorded at low level on the same track as audio—in this way the full width of the tape is available for the signal. The recorder comes complete with a new, miniature capacitor microphone, which could pass unnoticed as a tie-clip, or be hidden easily in the clothing. Sennheiser, also, have produced very compact microphones for similar applications.

Arriflex and Tandberg have co-operated in producing a new pilot-tone ¼in tape recorder.

FILM LIGHTING

Developments have been taking place in light-weight lighting units, specially for use on location. Until comparatively recently, feature films had to rely on heavy carbon-arc 'brutes' to provide fill-lighting to reduce the contrast of mid- and close-shots in sunshine, and also to act as a substitute sun for location close-shots in overcast conditions, and location or studio interiors. Apart from the weight of the lamp-heads and associated stands, arcs need a high-capacity dc supply, necessitating a special generator, and waste a large amount of power in dropper 'grids' which act as a ballast to stabilise the arc. Apart from their power, the arc's great advantage is that only minimum filtration is necessary to match daylight colour quality.

In the last few years, an alternative for some of the arc's applications has appeared, in the form of banks of sealed-beam tungsten-halogen lamps, known as 'minibrutes'; these are arranged in a single, light-weight sheet metal housing, with up to 12 lamps per unit. Lamps with integral dichroic filters are available for use in daylight, and can cast a powerful beam of light, specially useful for fill-in. They can also operate direct from 120 volt or 240 volt mains. However, they have some disadvantages: each bank tends to cast multiple shadows, and it is difficult to vary the spread of the light beam accurately (separate normal and wide-angle lamps can be fitted, and each half-bank can be converged and diverged in one direction only). In addition, operating costs can be high as the lamps have a limited life (30h).

Another, more conventional light-weight lamp for location and studio use is the Lowell Softlite—a folding unit that weighs only 3·2kg, but has a light output comparable to conventional units weighing more than five times as much. The saving in weight is effected by using a light aluminium yoke and frame, over which a reflector made of silvered, fabric-backed vinyl is fastened by Velcro tabs. Two 500 or 800 watt lamps fit into holders on a central, front strut. The whole unit, with barn-doors, folds into an attache-type case measuring 70×40×10cm and weighing 3·2kg. Thus the saving in weight when transporting lights to location can be considerable, and in addition the unit is cheaper than conventional soft-lights.

Developments have also taken place in conventional studio lamps. Pinewood Studios, which pioneered the introduction of pole-operated incandescent lamps for film production, has introduced a remote-controlled lamp in which all settings such as pan, tilt, focus, and barndoor setting (of each door separately, as well as rotation) can be power operated from a single motor. Setting can be done either from a small hand unit plugged into the appropriate lamp circuit on the grid, or from a control console switchable to operate all or most of the lamps on a set.

More powerful tungsten-halogen lamps and luminaires have been developed, Mole Richardson of Los Angeles producing 5 and 10kW units, and improvements have been made in some of the medium power lamps: Sylvania have manufactured extended life tungsten-halogen lamps with hard glass envelopes and incorporating krypton gas in the filling. GE of America have produced a single-ended 2kW Quartzline lamp for scoops etc, while Ianiro have used a double-ended 2kW lamp in a new, ultra-lightweight variable-focus flood.

Powerful, lightweight floodlamps have also been made by Kobold, Schneeberger and others utilising small, 575W HMI discharge lamps which—although they have a line spectrum—produce light which mixes quite well with daylight. Very high luminous efficiencies, of the order of 80 l/W, are obtained, and the 2¼kg lamp has an output of 46,000 lumens, giving around 4200 and 6000 Lux at 3m in the flood and spot positions respectively. The lamp can be filtered down to 3200K (effective) with a loss of only 20% of the light. Operation is from the mains via a 4kg control unit. A special starting circuit is contained in the lamp head, and the lamp takes about 1min to reach full output from cold.

Another lightweight floodlamp design was pioneered by Hedler in Germany. The very compact fitting is kept cool by a small blower. The Ventilux 1250 model takes a U-shaped t-h lamp up to 1250W, while the de Luxe 2000 takes two 650 or 1000W lamps. Thanks to the forced ventilation, there is no restriction to the time the lamp may be left switched on, while the noise is low enough not to interfere with sound pick-up on most outside locations.

MISC.

For viewing production rushes away from base, Samcine have imported a new, transportable Italian 35mm projector, the Pion, which has the facility of operating double-headed; thus it is possible to view sync rushes where the sound has been transferred to 35 sepmag.

Kodak have demonstrated a hot-wire splicing technique for polyester-based films, and have also introduced a new range of Ektalux A-D conversion filters made of cast resin for camera use.

Standards published during year appertaining to film production

Note: PH prefixes denote ANSI (American National Standards Institute) American National Standards; RP prefixes SMPTE Recommended Practices; ISO/R prefixes International Organisation for Standardisation Recommendations.

PH22.56 Draft: Nomenclature for Motion-Picture Film Used in Studios and Processing Laboratories.

PH22.106 Draft: Dimensions of Projectable Anamorphic Image Area on 35mm Motion-Picture Film, 2·35:1 Aspect Ratio.

PH22.124–1970: Specifications for Screen Luminance for Indoor Motion-Picture Theatres.

PH22.177–1970: Dimensions of Magnetic Striping of 35mm Motion-Picture Film for Four-track Magnetic Sound Release Prints.

RP 40 Proposed: Specifications for 35mm Projector Alignment and Screen Image Quality Test Film.

ISO/R 1039–1969: Dimensions of Cores for Motion-Picture and Magnetic Films.

APPLIED AND SCIENTIFIC CINEMATOGRAPHY

Arriflex introduced a new registration camera for medical, industrial and research work, the Arritechno 35. Two models give maximum speeds of 90 and 150pps respectively using single and double pull-down claws. Drive is by a printed-circuit disc motor, with fast start-up. Quick-change, fast load magazines hold 200ft of normal or 300ft of thin-based 35mm film.

Strobe Automation introduced a new strobe unit for microcinematography. Maurer introduced a new, small, portable processing machine for both 35 and 16mm film, perforated or unperforated, called the Maurer-Matic, using a monobath for developing and fixing followed by a rinse-stabiliser and hot-air drier. Only an electricity supply, not running water, is needed for operation. Operating temperature and speed is variable.

Improvements have been made to two motion analysing projectors, which in general can be programmed to advance the film frame by frame at pre-selected intervals to allow fast-moving phenomena to be studied. Kodak introduced the Analyst LW224A, and Old Delft a new version of the Analector, with a modified remote control unit with illuminated digital display of working speed and direction.

LABORATORY EQUIPMENT

Arriflex introduced a new colour analyser which operates on purely optical principles, allowing colour and density correction for printing to be estimated from one-light or two-frame test prints (or reversal originals in 16mm).

Liquid gates for optical printers were introduced by Contim, Producers Service Corporation/Acmade (distributed by Vinten in UK) and Neilson Hordell. By immersing the negative in a liquid having the same refractive index as the film, scratches and surface blemishes are largely eliminated. This is specially valuable in special effects work, and in blowing up 16mm and especially Super 16 to 35mm for wide-screen cinema presentation. PSC/Vinten also introduced the Spectra Film Gate Photometer, which allows white-light as well as red, green and blue illuminance to be read directly at the printer's film gate, in printer points, and also allows the uniformity of the field to be checked at nine positions in the gate. Probes are available for Acme, B & H Model C and other printers. The same firm also produced a focusing aid for optical printers, the Focatron.

Visnews Facilities introduced the SOS-Takita printers into the UK, while Eclair-Debrie took over Newman & Guardia and their range of Lawley processing machines.

16mm

While film series made for television, particularly those made by non-broadcast organisations, continue to be made largely on 35mm, direct 16mm production is becoming more commonplace. Advantages are partly due to lighter equipment giving faster set-up and wrapping times, lower freight charges and greater flexibility in use (as with the new, lighter, film production equipment mentioned above), and also in a considerable reduction in negative and print stock costs. In the UK, the 'Jason King' series was shot at EMI-MGM Elstree on Eclair NPR cameras fitted with Add-a-Vision TV viewfinders, and mounted in a blimp to reduce the noise level of the camera to studio standards.

It was announced at Film '71 that 95% of BBC's film shooting was on 16mm, and special techniques had to be developed to match the quality of film inserts into electronic-camera productions, A great improvement in sharpness, tone-range and colour is obtained using negative film in the telecine machine, and reversing it electronically during transfer to videotape. Prints are made only for cutting and viewing rushes, the original being neg-cut to match the cutting copy. By the use of TARIF controls, colour grading can be carried out during transfer. An advantage of this method is that it leaves the negative available for colour printing if copies are needed for foreign release etc.

16mm CAMERAS & MOTORS

Crystal-controlled motors and conversions for 16mm cameras were offered by several makers: Jensen made a crystal-control unit to fit on the outside of an Arri 16BL, which needed no internal modifications to be made to the camera, and also a replacement crystal motor for the Arri 16St.

Both Eclair and Perfectone produced crystal motors for the Eclair NPR which offer a choice of 24 or 25pps operation with 50, 60 or 100Hz pilot-tone outputs (for use with tape recorders not fitted with matched crystal oscillators) and also permit wild operation over a range of running speeds. A useful extra is that the camera always stops with the shutter open to the viewfinder—the cameraman's view is therefore not blacked out between shots.

A very compact, silent running camera was introduced by Eclair. Their ACL is almost a scaled-down version of the NPR, with a similar shape that sits well on the shoulder. A new, crystal-controlled brushless motor is used which is very much smaller than existing types, and enables the overall size to be reduced to $28 \times 18 \times 15$cm and the weight, complete with 6:1 zoom and 60m (200ft) magazine, to 3·8kg. A 0·45kg, 12 volt ni-cad battery can run up to 800m of film, and a new fast charger can re-charge the battery from flat in under 30min.

Pathé also showed the prototype of a new electronically controlled camera, in both 16 and double-Super-8 versions.

A number of new models also appeared, mostly in prototype form, specially designed for news sound shooting, which in the UK and USA normally utilises single-system sound on edge stripe. Many of these models were designed for 60m (200ft) spool loading, as this enables the overall size of the camera to be reduced appreciably; there is some argument among users whether this gives sufficient running time between re-loads for this type of work. Auricon produced a Newsvoice using their basic mechanism in conjunction with two 200ft spools in tandem mounted in a body designed to fit on the shoulder, but do not seem to be proceeding with construction. Cinema Product Developments are one of the firms who use the Auricon mechanism in cameras of their own make, and their CP-16 prototype is of conventional layout, but with a lightweight magnesium body and a short finder allowing the camera to sit well on the shoulder; the drive battery is built in. Beaulieu made a prototype for 200ft spools with automatic lacing, but at the time of writing they do not seem quite satisfied with it and are believed to be making modifications. The prototype had built-in battery supply, choice of crystal or electronic 24/25pps motors, power zooming of the interchangeable 12–120mm lens and fully-automatic exposure control, with a low profile designed to sit on the shoulder.

In contrast, the Canon Sound Scoopic 200 was a rather tall camera with the twin 200ft spools placed at the bottom, so that it could be pressed against the chest for stability.

It too had fully-auto exposure control and automatic lacing, but the 6:1 zoom lens was not interchangeable.

Several modifications were made to existing camera models to make them more versatile. Beaulieu offered a power-zoom version of their R16 Electric; the zooming speed could be varied over a wide range, and an override button zoomed the lens out to maximum focal length at full speed and opened up the aperture fully to allow easy focusing.

Visnews Facilities made conversions to Canon Scoopic cameras enabling them to generate pulses for double-system sound shooting, particularly with cassette tape recorders.

The Doiflex 16 camera was re-introduced in the UK in an improved version by Cintron, who also offered a stop-motion accessory for cartoon and trick work etc.

Paillard-Bolex introduced a new series of cameras in which the normal three-lens turret is replaced by a single, large breech-lock bayonet mount. This should give better support to heavy zoom and telephoto lenses. The basic SB model is for 100ft spool loading, while the SBM allows an external 400ft magazine to be fitted. The EBM with built-in governed electric motor was shown in prototype, and should become available during the current year.

Photosonics produced a hand-held camera for sports and scientific work which can operate at speeds up to 500fps.

George Mitchell, the veteran camera designer whose name is found on most cameras used to shoot cinema films the world over, has formed a new company, the Gamit Corporation, and has announced that he is building a revolutionary new 16mm camera (possibly to be followed by 35mm and even Super 8 models). He has always laid great stress on film steadiness, and he proposes to incorporate a new registration system that locates the film along the vertical axis, rather than the horizontal as heretofore. He intends to incorporate a new, high speed pull-down which will allow shutter openings of 300 degrees, thus cutting down the amount of light needed for a given lens aperture by 40%. His single-sided intermittent system will allow simple factory conversion of the camera from normal to Super 16.

This latter gauge is being increasingly used by producers in some countries as an original for subsequent blow-up to 35mm wide-screen for cinema release. By enlarging the gate aperture to cover what is normally the sound-track area (and re-centering the lens) a format is obtained which has similar proportions to the 1·65–1·8:1 used for wide-screen presentation, and which therefore needs significantly less magnification during the blow-up printing process. The new, faster Ektachrome Commercial, 7252, allows greatly improved quality to be obtained in the blow-ups. The system was started in the Scandinavian countries, whose producers have very restricted home markets, and who therefore had to find means of trimming budgets as much as possible. The Eclair NPR proved very suitable for modification to the new frame size, and at the time of writing Samuelson's have converted six of their cameras. Colour Film Services and Humphries Labs have installed wet-gate blow-up facilities for Super 16 to 35mm wide-screen.

As in 35mm, new faster and wider-angled lenses were introduced for 16mm cameras. These included 5·9mm f/1·8 and 28mm f/1·1 Angénieux, and a 180mm f/1·3 Zoomar fixed lenses, and new zooms from Angénieux (9·5–57mm f/1·6, focusing to 0·6m), Canon (whose 12–120mm f/2·2 Macro-zoom used two fluorite lens elements in its construction to reduce secondary spectrum), and new 10–100mm f/2 designs from Schneider and Zeiss.

Rank Precision Industries delivered the first production version of their image intensifier (to ITN) which allows filming in very low lighting conditions, even starlight. Old Delft showed a prototype at Film '71 of a more compact intensifier (using their own 3-stage 18mm tube in place of the 25mm tube used by Rank) which used a specially corrected field lens to overcome the pincushion distortion which seems inherent in intensifier tubes. They also showed a very compact single-stage version, with C-mounts at each end so that it could be screwed straight onto a camera and take the camera lens at its front end, which was said to have a gain equivalent to five stops, i.e. 32 times. Whether this gain is enough to overcome the loss of colour (the image is black and green) remains to be seen, although undoubtedly there will be applications where the device will prove useful.

Saft introduced a new range of VR nickel-cadmium cells with 20% increased capacity for a given size, and specially suitable for fast re-charging.

16mm SOUND
Rank introduced the Newsporta amplifier for the striped BL and similar cameras, catering for three inputs and having optional automatic level control. General Camera Corporation made a very compact two-input amplifier for the Cinevoice magnetic conversions, which can be switched to mic or line input, and allow manual mixing with VU meter or automatic level control.

New sync and slating systems were introduced, including a radio slate device from Kudelski (Nagra) which marked the tape with a code that interrupted the pilot tone signal and fogged film frames to match. Decoding could be carried out at the time of transfer to fully-coated magnetic by a QDAN unit with digital scene identification readout.

Uher brought out their new 1200 Report tape recorder with two microphone inputs and pilot-tone record and transfer capability in conjunction with their new W352 Synchroniser. The latter can be used for both forward and backward regulation during transfer. A special feature is that the transfer speed remains locked to the frequency of the last received pilot tone signal if this should drop out or fail for some reason.

For the smaller unit, and for amateurs also, a new Farnell-Tandberg Sync Indicator allows low-cost transfer to stripe or fully-coated film by manual regulation of Tandberg 11-1P or -2M tape recorders.

In Germany, Erlson built a prototype 16mm sepmag version of their perforated tape system, in which interlock to camera or projector is maintained by a special stepping motor and loop-sensing servo system, which regulates the speed of the friction drive applied to the tape. By this means only a very small load is placed on the perforations.

Ilford-Zonal introduced new tapes and magnetic films to the market. The System II films had new additives in the oxide coating (including tungsten disulphide which gives the film a characteristic black colour) that act as lubricants and reduce resistivity and static. The surface is polished for better head-life and improved high frequency response and a better noise characteristic is claimed. Both 5 thou acetate and 3 thou polyester based versions are available in all the usual widths and coats. Two professional magnetic tapes were also introduced under the Spectrum 1 label; one is specially formulated for low noise for master recordings ($\frac{1}{4}$ to 2in widths), and the other for low print-through characteristics. 1 and $1\frac{1}{2}$ thou acetate, pvc or polyester bases are available. Another new introduction from this firm was a series of magnetic heads for both tape and film in all widths and track configurations.

16mm PROJECTORS
With the trend towards smaller cinemas, and multiples produced by splitting some existing theatres (which often share one projection box) increasing numbers of exhibitors are turning towards 16mm projection, with its lower capital and running costs. New static 16mm projectors, almost invariably fitted with xenon lamp-houses, have appeared for this market, including models from Fumeo (handled in the UK by Westrex), Prevost (Heyden) and Bauer (Rank). The latter introduced an interesting Non-stop attachment for continuous showing without need for rewinding the film: Up to 4000m of film can be accommodated horizontally, on driven rollers, interwound with a protective plastic film that minimises surface damage as the layers slide over one another in the coil.

Most of these projectors have provision for fitting anamorphic lenses for presenting 'scope films. A new, low-cost A-lens has appeared which is equally suitable for portable 16mm machines, the British made Centamorphot, distributed by the Widescreen Centre.

The greater use of 16mm for exhibition has also had its effects on distributors. As any damage to the film is relatively more serious in the smaller gauge, thorough inspection is advisable to prevent any incipient trouble from spreading. Paulmar, who have been offering an automatic film inspection machine for some time, introduced a twin version capable of dealing with two films at a time, thus allowing a quicker turn-round to be achieved.

Various new double-band machines have appeared, aimed mainly at the smaller production company or agency, for use in dubbing and review theatres. These handle 16mm fully-coated magnetic film on a mechanism plate forming the off-side of the projector, and several allow both recording and replay from centre or edge sepmag, and transfer between this and commag and comopt. Both transports are driven from the same motor, usually of the synchronous type, and with some models it is possible to couple up further sepmag units for full-scale dubbing.

New double-band projectors that have appeared during the year include the Bauer P6 Studio, the Hokushin-PAG Polestar, and the Hortson Series 70.

Standards published during year appertaining to 16mm

PH22.43–1970:	Specifications for 16mm 3-kHz Flutter Test Film, Photographic Type.
PH22.83 Draft:	Location and Spacing of Edge Numbers on 16mm Motion-Picture Film.
RP 41–1970:	Colour and Luminance of Review Room Screens Used for 16mm Colour Television Prints.
ISO/R 890–1968:	Location and Width of the Recording Head for Centre Sound Records on 16mm Perforated Magnetic Film.
ISO/R 891–1968:	Location and Width of the Recording Head for Edge Sound Records on 16mm Perforated Magnetic Film.
ISO/R 1019–1969:	Dimensions of Daylight Loading Spools for 16mm Motion-Picture Films.

16mm EDITING EQUIPMENT
Cutting tables of a new type were introduced by Atema of Sweden and Magnasync/Moviola of the USA, both providing improved sound reproduction. The Atema table, in fact, was said to double as a recorder-reproducer, and with a small accessory could be used for transfer of pilot-tone recordings. The lacing path of the film, however, seemed a little too complicated for use as an editing machine. The main features of the Moviola Console Editor

were electronic digital indication of film footage which could be converted by a logic unit into minutes and seconds at the touch of a switch, and simple, drop-in loading of each film path; the sound quality was similar to that obtained from professional sound projectors, so that one could get a good idea of the sound that could be expected from the final soundtrack. Steenbeck introduced a special cutting table which displayed two pictures side by side, to allow cutting points from multi-camera takes to be found quickly.

SUPER 8mm
Professional Super 8 Uses

Increasing interest is being shown by television stations around the world in using Super 8 film for programming, specially for news programmes in some of the smaller stations (such as the cable-tv companies in the USA). Some have even experimented with commercials shot on this gauge. One snag has been the non-availability of professional equipment for Super 8, specially for sound shooting and editing. Bauer have shown a prototype Synchron 25 camera, which was, in fact, one of their top-line models modified for 25pps drive by a crystal-controlled motor; it could therefore be used for sound shooting in conjunction with a tape recorder using a matched crystal to lay down a pilot-tone control track. Beaulieu modified their 4008ZM camera to accept a pilot-tone generator.

KEM and Steenbeck produced editing tables for Super 8 picture and 16mm sepmag track which could be used for such work. The availability of such professional facilities should do much to make Super 8 more acceptable in the tv field.

Arriflex are believed to have made an experimental Super 8 camera, loaded with 100ft single-run spools, but no details have been released at the time of writing. George Mitchell of Gamit is thinking of developing a professional camera in this gauge.

With an eye on the professional market, two very long range zooms were introduced: Nikon had a 20:1 (6–120mm, f/1·8) prototype at photokina, while Canon showed a prototype 'Future' camera fitted with a 7–140mm f/1·8–2·2 lens, which incorporated two fluorite elements, and a range-finder system which worked independently of the focal length setting of the lens. They also introduced a 100ft spool-loading double-Super 8 version of their Scoopic.

Both the UK broadcasting organisations have on occasion transmitted 8mm news film where that was the only record available, and the BBC have transmitted amateur 8mm films successfully. In Canada, CBC have reported an experiment in using Super 8 for production work, and in the USA NBC believe that in 2–3 years significant amounts of Super 8 film will be used in tv.

New printers for producing Super 8 copies were introduced by Arri (35:4×S8) and Bell & Howell (16:2×S8 contact or continuous optical reduction); the latter also introduced a high speed sound transfer machine for magnetic sound on this gauge, while in Germany the educational authorities are proposing to standardise on Super 8 films with an optical sound track—Bauer have modified one of their projectors to take this.

Amateur Super 8

Although many new camera models have been introduced, most continue the basic pattern established in past years—reflex zooms with TTL exposure meters, often whole families of related cameras from one maker differing mainly in the zoom range and a few extra features. More attention seems to have been given to styling.

Several new models featured focusing to extremely close distances—the so-called macro range—generally by displacing one of the internal lens elements so as to upset the tracking of the zoom lens; by operating the zoom control, objects right up to the front glass of the lens could be brought into sharp focus. This feature was included in the top-of-the-range models from Cinemax, Elmo, Eumig/Bolex and Vivitar. Elmo also had an alternative, novel approach: Swinging out a small mirror on the side of their Super 103T camera imaged a title or slide placed in a frame adjacent to the zoom lens on to the film via a beam-splitting prism in the optical system (which also served to divert light to the viewfinder). This could be superimposed on the scene taken in by the normal zoom lens, though the latter could be capped if only a straight ultra-close-up was required.

Elmo also introduced a 3-D attachment for one of their cameras, using five mirrors. For projection it could be fitted with polaroid filters, the audience viewing through polarising spectacles. The images were turned through 90deg and arranged toe to toe on the film, which helped to prevent uneven illumination of the two images, but made worse the effects of film unsteadiness. With the small Super 8 frame it seemed difficult to get enough definition and light for really satisfactory projection.

Bauer, who, with their C Royal, pioneered limited backwind in Super 8 cameras to permit dissolves to be made, added two more cameras in this range with different zoom ratios, and also incorporated this facility in two models they built for Rollei. This idea was taken a stage further by Agfa–Gevaert (who had prototype cameras built for them by Minolta in Japan) and Nizo, who incorporated a push-button dissolve facility, which Bauer could only approximate by a clip-on accessory. This latter also allowed time-lapse filming at pre-determined intervals from a fraction of a second to several minutes—a facility which Nizo have been fitting for some time in their cameras, and have now extended to allow time exposures to be made automatically (for coping with static subjects in very poor light conditions).

Sankyo introduced a new range of 'Hi-focus' Super 8 cameras with a quick-focusing rangefinder facility: By pulling back on the focusing ring the normal reflex finder view is replaced by twin rangefinder images of contrasting colours, which can be quickly brought into co-incidence at the subject by rotating the focus ring. The advantage over the normal focusing aids fitted to cine cameras is that it is not necessary to zoom out the lens to its longest focal length for focusing, and thereafter re-set it for the shot.

Agfa, Eumig and Bolex have also produced some very small, almost pocket, zoom reflex models.

Ferrania and Turaphot have introduced daylight-balanced Super 8 film in cartridges, although there would seem to be little cause for this as all Super 8 cameras incorporate a conversion filter for using Type A film in daylight, which in most cases operates automatically. In fact, daylight film could cause trouble on some models that do not have fully automatic filter-sensing.

Russia introduced their first Super 8 cameras, both in standard cartridge and double-run spool loading.

Fuji introduced two new cameras for the Single 8 system, one of which used a novel exposure metering circuit incorporating a silicon solar cell, followed by a fet and integrated circuit amplifier.

Renewed interest seems to have been paid to sync-sound shooting by amateurs. Bell and Howell have added two new cameras for their Filmosound 8 system. Synchronex Corporation are now offering three cameras and two cassette tape recorders for their system, which involves transfer to stripe at the processing lab before the film is returned to the user. Chinon and Elmo are introducing their own sync systems, using a cassette and reel-to-reel recorder respectively. Nizo and Zeiss are offering cameras with built-in contacts for the Volland Universal system (which needs one pulse per four frames). In the UK, new sync equipment has been introduced by Contronics (pulse) and Filmin (perf tape). It is reported that the latter system is being tried out in the USA for television. Filmin have also brought out a cutting aid for perforated tape, their Editer, which is used with an animated viewer and contains a magnetic head and sprockets which interlock film and tape motion; the head can be slid along the baseboard to help find and correct any sync errors.

Super 8 Projectors

In projectors, interesting audio-visual models were introduced by Kodak and De Jur in the USA. They could be coupled to tape recorders and pre-programmed to stop and show a still frame (by a cue printed on the film) without loss of brightness, and hold this until re-started manually or by a cue from the control track on the tape. With suitably prepared material, this has advantages that considerable film footage can be saved while tables, diagrams etc are explained on the sound track, and possibly held by the pupil for further study; further, a still frame will be steadier and hence more legible than the same information presented from moving film.

In both the a-v and amateur field, several new cartridge-load projectors were introduced, with a bewildering variety of cartridge types, most suited only to a particular maker's machines. The only ones to make much impact were the Fairchild 70 series, which use a new endless-loop cartridge for striped Super 8 film which now has the standard +18 frames sound separation, and the Technicolor 1300 Sound Movie Viewer for optical track Super 8, which is well suited as an aid to personal study, and has been adopted by the Open University for use in its study centres. Another new introduction intended for similar purposes, and also using optical sound Super 8 was the Fujics TM40. Taking its own cartridge or spools, this uses continuously moving film with rotating polygon image compensation to produce a stationary image; avoiding intermittent pull-down should materially increase the life of prints.

Less development than expected has taken place in the 'open' (i.e. non-loop) cartridge systems, with neither of the two main contenders—B & H Auto 8 and Kodak—finding much favour in practice. Apart from one machine from B & H, the Auto 8 cassette has only been used by Bauer for one silent and one sound projector (T20 and T25) which have not yet appeared on the market, prototypes from Agfa and Noris, and two prototype Super 8 'telecines' intended for replaying films via a tv set (Bauer, Nordmende). The Kodak cartridge has been adopted by Eumig, who are the only people actively selling cartridge projectors at the time of writing; they offer one sound and one dual-gauge silent model, and are about to be joined by Bolex (now virtually part of the Eumig organisation) with a very similar Super 8-only mute version. (They are also making a model for their own design of EP cartridge, the Multimatic.) Kodak have re-styled their cartridges (badly needed, as they compared badly in appearance with Auto 8s), but do not seem to be pushing their two cartridge machines, which have been available for some time. The minor US manufacturers do not seem able to make up their minds, and some seem to be backing both horses—in prototype form at least. The Japanese have so far produced no hardware for either system, but Elmo have pioneered a cartridge of their own design. At the time of writing, the situation remains fluid.

In Germany, Ullstein A-V have announced that they will soon begin distributing sponsored medical films to doctors on Super 8 with optical sound in Auto 8 cassettes, but no announcement has been made about the source of projectors for this scheme.

Standards appertaining to 8 and Super 8 published during year

PH22.153 Draft:	Printed Area in Super 8 Printing on 16/8mm Film Perforated 1–4.
PH22.166–1970:	Specifications for Super 8 Motion-Picture Film Camera Cartridge Notches for Exposure Control and Stock Identification.
PH22.182 Draft:	Dimensions for Photographic Sound Record on Super 8 Motion-Picture Prints.
RP 42–1970:	Emulsion Orientation of Super 8 Release Prints.
ISO/R 892–1968:	Dimensions of Projection Reels for 8mm Motion-Picture Film (other than Type S).
ISO/R 1020–1969:	Dimensions of Daylight Loading Spools for Double-8mm Motion-Picture Film.

In addition, RP 28–1968: Dimensions for 35mm Motion-Picture Film Perforated 8mm, 5R-1500 was withdrawn because the specifications were not being followed.

Cassettes and other image storing systems

Although much publicity has been given during the year to various competing cassette systems not using conventional film and intended for replaying recordings through normal tv sets in the home, classroom and industry, none of them have reached the marketing stage as of mid-1971.

The first one likely to become available is the EVR system backed by CBS and CIBA—the only one for which a significant amount of software (programmes) is in production. The plant set up by Ilford Limited at Basildon has been producing black-and-white cassettes for some months, and Rank Bush Murphy have been building the necessary teleplayers. Licences for the EVR system have been taken up by concerns in most parts of Europe and several major firms in Japan. The system uses a small flying-spot scanner to read one of two silver-image tracks recorded on a continuously moving 8·75mm wide film, which also carries magnetic stripe soundtracks.

None of the other systems seems out of the research and development stage. RCA's Selectavision, which uses a low-powered laser to read a recording impressed on a thin vinyl tape is reported to have run into difficulties, apparently with the laser.

Teldec's (Telefunken and Decca) Videodisc, using a thin, stamped vinyl disc which is supported on an air cushion, rotated at 1500rpm and read electro-mechanically by a special diamond-tipped pick-up, has not got out of the demonstration stage. The system records the waveform of the tv signal as hill and dale microgroove impressions, and carries sound as pulse-code modulation in the line-sync blanking.

The main videotape cartridge systems—Sony's Videocassette and Avco's Cartrivision in Japan, Ampex's Instavideo in the USA, and Philips' VCR in Europe—also seem hardly out of the development stage. Almost none of the competing systems are compatible with one another, and most use recordings that are specific to one tv standard, so different versions are needed for Europe and USA/Japan, for instance.

At present it seems doubtful if there will be a market for more than a few of them. Here, too, the situation remains open.

STUDENTS' SECTION

ANDREW SEYMOUR:
GUILDFORD COLLEGE OF ART

MEIRA HAND: LONDON COLLEGE OF PRINTING

FRANCOIS GUILLET
BOURNEMOUTH COLLEGE OF ART

BYRON NEWMAN ▶
LONDON COLLEGE OF PRINTING

ABOVE: MARK TROMPETELLER (LONDON COLLEGE OF PRINTING)   BELOW: JOHN COWPER (TRENT POLY)

GILL SMYTH (LONDON COLLEGE OF PRINTING)

◀JOHN LONDEI (MEDWAY COLLEGE OF ART)

RAY MASSEY (MEDWAY COLLEGE OF ART)

Formulae for Colour and Black and White Processing

Contents

COLOUR-GENERAL INSTRUCTIONS

Making up solutions
Glass, plastic, new enamel or stainless-steel vessels should be used. The chemicals should be taken in order and each completely dissolved before adding the next, using about three-quarters of the final volume of water. Cold or tepid (35-40°C) water should be used, *not* hot water (exceptions are given below). Distilled or deionised water should preferably be used in making up the solutions, particularly the first and colour developers, but this is not essential, and tap water may be used. If the water supply is too hard, it is helpful to add, particularly to water destined for black-and-white and colour developers, *before* dissolving any other chemicals, 2gm/l of a sequestrating agent: Calgon, sodium hexametaphosphate or sodium tripolyphosphate.

Crystalline carbonate should be dissolved separately in about three times its own bulk of hot water. Hot water must also be used to make up a hardener-bleach, which may throw down a white precipitate when cold, but this does not affect its working; stop baths are best made up cold. Time can be saved by using 20% solutions of thiocyanate and bromide instead of solid reagent. Phenidone is preferably dissolved in a little warm water before adding to the rest of the solution.

All solutions should be allowed to stand for about 30min and filtered before use.

Activity
When strict accuracy is essential, the pH-value may be checked with a pH-meter (test papers are not suitable) and adjusted to the standard value by the addition of caustic soda (sodium hydroxide) pellets or flakes—rather than sticks, which are dangerous—to raise the pH-value or, if necessary, sodium bisulphite or acetic acid to lower it.

Storage
The keeping time of used solutions may be diminished by 20-65% depending upon conditions of use and storage (fullness and sealing of bottles, darkness and temperature). Well stoppered dark glass or polythene bottles should be used at temperatures not exceeding 20°C. However, first and colour developers should, in any case, be used as fresh as possible. If bleach and fixer are made up as triple-strength stocks, they will be found to have excellent storage properties.

Temperature
Maintenance of constant temperature throughout first (black-and-white) development in reversal processing and (colour) development in negative processing is absolutely essential if consistent results are to be achieved. In the other solutions, the tolerance is wider, although the specified limits should be respected. Even so, it is important that excessive temperature differences between successive solutions and wash water, especially in transferring to the wash following colour development, be avoided, otherwise there is a risk of reticulation. The washing times given in the procedures apply to temperatures below 18°C; at higher temperatures (20-24°C), they may be shortened without ill effect by 20-40%, thus substantially reducing the overall processing time.

Times
All times, including those for washing or rinsing, should be adhered to in order to obviate the possibility of colour casts. The specified treatment times include 10-15sec drainage.

Agitation
The recommended agitation is indicated immediately after the procedure. It should be adhered to strictly in the developers but in the other solutions should be regarded as a minimum: more vigorous agitation can be only advantageous in expediting solution changes in the emulsion.

Lighting
The individual procedures clearly show at what stage normal room lighting may be resumed when use of an open processing tank necessitates initial darkroom working. At the same stage, the lid of a light-tight tank may be removed.

Second exposure
The recommended lamp wattage and distance are shown at the appropriate point in the procedure. The film should preferably be removed from the spiral and see-sawed through a dish of cold water below the lamp, front and back being exposed approximately equally. If the exposure is carried out with the film in a transparent-ended spiral, best immersed in cold water in a white bowl, the time should be extended 1½ (35mm) or 2¼ (120) times. Care should be taken not to splash the hot lamp with water and not to work near the sink or taps unless the lampholder is properly earthed.

Wetting agents
If a final wash completes the procedure, the material should be passed for about 1min through water containing around 1gm/l of wetting agent in order to accelerate draining and drying, thereby inhibiting drying marks. The wetting agent may be either of the anionic type—e.g. American Cyanamid Aerosol OT (sodium di-iso octylsulphosuccinate), Union Carbide Tergitol 7 and Ciba Invitol—or the nonionic type—e.g. Rohm and Haas Triton X-100, Francolor Sunaptol OP and Union Carbide Tergitol NPX. The wetting agent is

conveniently stored as a 10% solution and made up as a 10% solution, thus forming a 1% solution. The working-strength solution keeps indefinitely but should be discarded after use.

Drying Should be performed under protection from air currents and accessibility of dust.

General Normally, the formulae quoted produce results closely corresponding with those from official kits, but deviations occasionally occur owing to variations in reagents from different suppliers. To compensate for these, where necessary, or to provide controls to suit the individual user's taste, the following notes on the less usual ingredients in some of the solutions may be helpful:

Citrazinic acid (CZA or 2,6-dihydroxy-isonicotinic acid) acts as a specialised restraining agent and serves to prevent what would otherwise be an excessively dense and contrast dye image. A deficiency produces a dense greenish image, but an excess produces a thin pinkish image; a 10% change in concentration shows markedly in the result.

Ethylenediamine tetra-acetic acid disodium salt (EDTA salt) acts as an accelerator. A deficiency produces a thin yellowish image, whereas an excess produces a heavy bluish image; a 10% variation is quite noticeable.

Benzyl alcohol acts as a penetrating agent making the otherwise waterproof dye-former particles accessible to the colour developer products. It is particularly important to ensure that this liquid is completely dissolved before any other reagent of the colour developer is added.

CD3 is the Kodak designation for 4-amino-N-ethyl-N-(methanosulphamido-ethyl)-m-toluidine Sesquisulphate monohydrate, and in moderate quantities is most easily obtained as Mydochrome (May & Baker) or Merck Colour Developer No. 3. Variations in amount produce effects rather similar to those of the EDTA salt, the balance travelling from thin and warm to dense and cool as the concentration is increased.

Precaution Colour developers contain a derivative of paraphenylenediamine, which in certain persons may produce a form of skin irritation. Persons who are sensitive to chemicals of this kind should take precautions to avoid contact with the developer, by using rubber gloves. In all cases, when the skin has been in contact with the solution, it should be rinsed well in clean water, preferably made acid with a few drops of acetic or hydrochloric acid, before using soap.

REVERSAL COLOUR PROCESSING

AGFACOLOR CT18 and CK20

This material made by Agfa-Gevaert at Leverkusen in West Germany has a rated sensitivity of ASA50, 18DIN, and is balanced for daylight of 5500°K. Supplied in all the usual formats including sheet film for professional use, it is a subtractive material and the emulsion has colourless non-diffusing couplers incorporated. Agfacolor remains based on the original work done by Schneider and his collaborators beginning in 1936. The corresponding film in artificial light of 3200°K is Agfacolor CK20, ASA80, 20DIN, whose processing is identical.
General instructions pp. 205-6

Formulae
First developer (pH: $10 \cdot 2 \pm 0 \cdot 1$)

Metol	3·5gm
Sodium sulphite anhydrous	40·0gm
Hydroquinone	7·0gm
Sodium carbonate anhydrous	40·0gm
Sodium thiocyanate	1·8gm
Potassium bromide	2·0gm
Potassium iodide, 0·1% solution	6·0ml
Nitrobentimidatole nitrate 0·2% solution	20·0ml
Water to	1000·0ml

Stop bath (pH: $5 \cdot 2 \pm 0 \cdot 2$)

Acetic acid 100%	10·0ml
Sodium acetate crystalline	30·0ml
Water to	1000·0ml

Colour developer (pH: $10 \cdot 8 \pm 0 \cdot 1$)

Calgon, tripolyphosphate	2·0gm
Sodium sulphite	2·0gm
Potassium carbonate anhydrous	50·0gm
Hydroxylamine sulphate	2·5gm
or hydrochloride	2·2gm
Potassium bromide	1·0gm

Add before use:

Droxychrome or Activol X	6·0gm
(or the equivalent quantity of a 20% solution)	
Water to	1000·0ml

One may also use as the colour developing agent Diethyl-paraphenylenediamine sulphate or hydrochloride (Activol 7 or 6 or even Genochrome or Activol number 1) may also be used at 4·5gm per litre).

Bleach (pH: $5 \cdot 2 \pm 0 \cdot 2$)

Potassium ferricyanide	80·0gm
Potassium bromide	20·0gm
Disodium phosphate crystalline 7H$_2$O	20·0gm
Sodium or potassium bisulphate	12·0gm
Water to	1000·0ml

Ferrania formula VC212 may also be used, see under Ferraniacolor.

Fixer (pH: $6 \cdot 5 \pm 8 \cdot 5$)

Sodium thiosulphate crystalline	200·0gm
Sodium sulphite anhydrous	10·0gm
Water to	1000·0ml

Ammonium thiosulphate, 120gm per litre, may be used to accelerate fixing.

Stabiliser and wetting agent	
Wetting agent 10% solution	5–10ml
Formalin 35–40% solution	10·0ml
Water to	1000·0ml

Procedure

1	First developer	17–19min 20±0·5°C
2	Rinse	15sec 16–20°C
3	Stop bath	4min 18–20°C
4	Wash	10min 16–20°C
5	Re-exposure, 500W, 1min each side at 1 yard	2min
6	Colour developer	14min 20±0·5°C
7	Wash	20min 16–20°C
8	Bleach	5min 18–20°C
9	Wash	5min 16–20°C
10	Fixer	5min 18–20°X
11	Final wash	10min 16–20°C
12	Stabiliser and wetting agent	1min 18–20°C
13	Dry	— 30°C max
	Total	92–94min

AGFACHROME FILM AND SHEET S50 and L50

Procedure

		At 20°C	At 24°C
1	First developer	18–20min 20±0·5°C	13–14min 24±0·25°C
2	Rapid rinse	30sec 16–20°C	30sec 20–24°C
3	Stop bath	4min 18–20°C	3min 22–24°C
4	Wash	10min 16–20°C	7min 20–24°C
5	Re-exposure	500W at one yard	
6	Colour developer	14min 20±0·5°C	11min 24±0·25°C
7	Wash	20min 16–20°C	14min 20–24°C
8	Bleach	5min 18–20°C	4min 22–24°C
9	Wash	5min 16–20°C	4min 20–24°C
10	Fixer	5min 18–20°C	4min 22–24°C
11	Wash	10min 16–20°C	7min 20–24°C
12	Stabiliser and wetting agent	1min 16–20°C	1min 20–24°C
13	Dry	Maximum 30°C	

Formulae: same as for CT18

EKTACHROME E2*†

Although the Kodak chemical kits for the Improved E2-process are no longer available and the process itself is officially regarded as obsolete, many readers are successfully using solutions made up according to the following formulae to process the various Ektachrome materials. It should be noted, however, that some quality will be sacrificed for ease of working and ready availability of chemicals.

General Instructions pp. 205-6

Formulae
First developer

Metol	5·0gm
Sodium sulphite, anhydrous	25·0gm

*Thompson C. L.—The British Journal of Photography, 15 November 1957 and 8 July 1960.

Hydroquinone	5·0gm
Sodium carbonate, anhydrous	25·0gm
or crystalline	70·0gm
Potassium bromide, 20% solution	10·0ml
Potassium iodide, 0·1% solution	10·0ml
Potassium thiocyanate, 20% solution	10·0ml
Johnson 142	5·0ml
Water to	1000·0ml

Hardener

Chrome alum	30·0gm
Water to	1000·0ml

Colour developer

Benzyl alcohol	5·0ml
Sodium sulphite, anhydrous	5·0gm
Sodium hydroxide, pellets	5·0gm
Trisodium phosphate, crystalline	25·0gm
CD3 or Mydochrome	10·0gm
Ethylenediamine tetra-acetic acid disodium salt	8·0gm
Citrazinic acid	1·2gm
Potassium bromide	1·0gm
Water to	1000·0ml

Clearing bath

Acetic acid, glacial	10·0ml
Sodium acetate, crystalline	10·0gm
Water to	1000·0ml

Bleach

Potassium ferricyanide	50·0gm
Potassium thiocyanate	7·5gm
Potassium bromide	15·0gm
Disodium phosphate, crystalline	1·5gm
Water to	1000·0ml

Fixer

Hypo, crystalline	150·0gm
Sodium bisulphite	15·0gm
Water to	1000·0ml

Stabiliser

Formalin, 40% formaldehyde	25·0ml
Johnson 326 (wetting agent)	5·0ml
Water to	1000·0ml

Procedure

1	First developer	10min* 24±0·25°C
2	Rinse	1min 22–26°C
3	Hardener	3min 22–26°C
4	Wash	5min 22–26°C
5	Re-exposure	—
6	Colour developer	15min 24±0·25°C
7	Wash	5min 22–26°C
8	Clear	5min 22–26°C
9	Wash	5min 22–26°C
10	Bleach	8min 22–26°C
11	Rinse	1min 22–26°C
12	Fixer	6min 22–26°C
13	Wash	8min 22–26°C
14	Stabiliser	1min 22–26°C
15	Dry	—
	Total	73min

*13min for 2X speed increase.

EKTACHROME E3

Note: The E3 Process is also usable with E2 and E4 materials (Ektachrome EX, EH and EHB).

Introduction

Supplied as sheet film, E3 replaced the E1 emulsion, which is no longer manufactured. The normal speed rating is ASA 50 but the rollfilms which the author has used have been rated at ASA 64; moreover, accompanying each carton of Daylight Type is a note indicating the speed and appropriate compensation filter for use with electronic flash, the speed and other characteristics of each batch being accurately checked before leaving the factory. Type B has a speed of ASA 32 with lamps of colour temperature 3200°K for an exposure of $\frac{1}{2}$sec.

As compared with E1, the resolving power and grain have undergone spectacular improvements, as also has the colour rendering. The latter is particularly striking by comparison with the E2 emulsion; greenish yellows (citron yellow) and greens are exceptionally pure and truthful. The same is true of reds, the most subtle shades of which are faithfully reproduced. Consequently this material is particularly suitable for photomechanical reproduction.

The E3 processing procedure differs from that of E2 Improved in that it employs a black-and-white developer of new type based upon the use of Phenidone (1-phenyl-3-pyrazolidone).

General Instructions pp. 205-6

Formulae

First developer (pH: 10·2–10·4)

Phenidone (or metol 6gm)*	0·5gm
Hydroquinone	6·0gm
Sodium carbonate, anhydrous	40·0gm
Sodium sulphite, anhydrous	40·0gm
Potassium bromide	2·0gm
Sodium thiocyanate	2·0gm
Potassium iodide†	0·006gm
6-nitrobenzimidazole nitrate, 0·2% solution	15·0ml
Water to	1000·0ml

Hardener-stop bath (pH: 3·5±2·2)

Chrome alum	30·0gm
Water (cold) to	1000·0ml

Clearing bath (pH: 4·6±0·2)

Potassium metabisulphite	20·0gm
Water to	1000·0ml

Bleach (same as for E4)

Fixer (pH: 4·7±0·2)

Sodium thiosulphate, crystalline‡	160·0gm
Potassium metabisulphite	20·0gm
Water to	1000·0ml

Colour developer (pH: 11·5±0·1)

Trisodium phosphate, crystalline, 12H$_2$O	40·0gm
Caustic soda, pellets	8·6gm
Sodium sulphite, anhydrous	5·0gm
Benzyl alcohol	5·0ml
EDTA No. 4	3·0gm
Ethylenediamine sulphate	7·5gm
Potassium iodide	0·01gm
Citrazinic acid (2·6 dihydroxyisonicotinic acid)	1·3gm
CD3	10·0gm
Water to	1000·0ml

Stabiliser

Formaldehyde, 35–40% solution	2·0ml
Wetting agent, 10% solution	10·0ml
Water to	1000·0ml

*Phenidone gives a warmer colour balance than metol.
†Optional.
‡or Ammonium thiosulphate 120·0gm.

Procedure

1	First developer	10min 24 ± 0·25°C
2	Rinse	$\frac{1}{2}$–1min 20–26°C
3	Hardener-stop bath	3–10min 20–26°C
	Normal room lighting may be resumed	
4	Wash, running water	3min 20–26°C
5	Re-exposure, No 2 photoflood at 1f	2×$\frac{1}{4}$min
6	Colour developer	15min 20–26°C
7	Wash, running water	5min 20–26°C
8	Clear	5min 20–26°C
9	Rinse, running water	5min 20–26°C
10	Bleach	8min 20–26°C
11	Rinse, running water	1min 20–26°C
12	Fixer	4min 20–26°C
13	Wash, running water	8min 20–26°C
14	Stabiliser	1min 20–26°C
15	Dry	— 45°C max
	Total	65–72min

Notes

A Recommended agitation is 5sec every minute.

B After Stage 5, the processing may be interrupted and the film dried, processing being completed later. In this case, washing should be prolonged to 5min, and the re-exposure to artificial light may be dispensed with. Once dry, the film should be kept in darkness to obviate any possibility of solarisation. If the intermediate drying procedure is followed it is *not* necessary to wet the film before proceeding to Stage 6.

C The CD3 should be added to the colour developer just before use, as the complete solution does not keep well (at most 15 days in unused condition). A violet coloration will be observed, which disappears after an interval of a few hours and is of no significance. The CD3 may be added either in the form of a powder or a 20% solution, of which the necessary quantity can be added before use with a pipette or measure:

EKTACHROME E4[*]

Introduction

The rapid progress of colour photography and the continuous pressure towards more mechanisation in processing have led the sensitised-materials manufacturers to an intensive study of methods of accelerated working to enable them to keep pace with the constantly increasing demand and to ensure the execution of orders in a reasonable time. This increase in productivity, despite continual increases in costs (labour, maintenance, rents and depreciation of investments), enables prices to be kept within limits acceptable to an ever-increasing amateur market.

The technology of manufacture of photographic materials has made great progress over the past few years, and it is now possible to produce emulsions of appreciably better mechanical resistance, which permit working at temperatures hitherto unthinkable in this sphere. The physicochemical reactions of photographic processing are subject to the same laws as elsewhere: they are notably accelerated by an increase in temperature. The speed increases by a factor of about 2·4 for an increase of 10°C, and the photochemical industry is now able to take full advantage of this possibility of improving the economic aspect of the processing procedure.

The Kodak E4 process was designed a priori for the mechanised processing of Ektachrome materials (EX, EH, Reversed Print, Infrared Aero) with the exception of professional-type films (processed by the E3 method), but it may also be used for hand processing, provided scrupulous attention is paid to the times of treatment in the respective baths. These times have been notably shortened in comparison with those of the E2/E3 procedures, but this very fact introduces greater risks for the amateur should he fail to observe them meticulously.

Process E4 presents two interesting peculiarities:
(i) Re-exposure before colour development has been discontinued; reversal is effected by chemical fogging of the emulsion during colour development. This solution contains an organic chemical—TBAB (tertiary butylaminoborane)—which enables all parts of the emulsion which have not been developed by the black-and-white first developer to react to the colour developer. TBAB is very toxic and must be handled with the greatest care to avoid contact with the skin and respiratory organs. It should be noted, however, that in the substitute formula for the colour developer this additive may be dispensed with, provided the film is re-exposed to light in the customary fashion; the colour characteristics of the film are practically unaffected. Chemical reversal with TBAB is also possible when working at 24°C (E3) but only with Ektachrome EX, EH and Infrared Aero.

(ii) To improve the mechanical resistance of emulsions destined for Process E4 treatment at 29°C, it is necessary to treat them in a preliminary hardening bath containing, in addition to formaldehyde, 2,5-dimethoxytetrahydrofuran (DMTF), a liquid whose vapour is very aggressive in its action upon the respiratory system and eyes, and is very rapidly absorbed by the cutaneous tissues. It is therefore essential to avoid any contact with the liquid. Should the skin become contaminated with it, the affected part should be very thoroughly washed for 15min. Should the eyes exhibit symptoms of irritation a doctor should immediately be consulted. So far as formaldehyde is concerned, amateurs will already be familiar with its very active tanning and

irritant properties, and we are confident that they will automatically take the utmost precautions against breathing the vapour or allowing the skin to come into contact with the solution.

Special attention is drawn to the author's warnings as to the extreme noxious nature of some of the chemicals used in these formulae. Their use should not be attempted by workers unaccustomed to handling such chemicals.

Procedure

1	Preliminary hardener	3min	29·5±0·5°C
2	Neutraliser	1min	28–31°C
3	First developer	6¼min	29·5±0·25°C
4	First stop bath	1¾min	28–31°C
	Normal room lighting may be resumed		
5	Wash, running water	4min	27–32°C
6	Colour developer	9min	27–32°C
7	Second stop bath	3min	27–32°C
8	Wash, running water	3min	27–32°C
9	Bleach	5min	27–32°C
10	Fixer	4min	27–32°C
11	Wash, running water	6min	27–32°C
12	Stabiliser	1min	27–32°C
13	Dry	—	43°C max
	Total	47min	

General Instructions pp. 205-6

Formulae

Pre-hardener (pH 4·9–5·0)

Sodium or potassium bisulphate	0·8gm
2,5-dimethoxytetrahydrofuran	5·0ml
Sodium sulphate, anhydrous	136·0gm
Formaldehyde, 35–40%, formalin	30·0ml
Potassium bromide	16·0gm
Water to	1000·0ml

Neutraliser (pH: 5·1–5·2)

Acetic acid, 100%	1·5ml
Sodium acetate, crystalline	24·0gm
Potassium bromide	17·0gm
Sodium sulphate, anhydrous	25·0gm
Potassium metabisulphite, crystalline	30·0gm
Water to	1000·0ml

First developer (pH: 10·1–10·3)

Calgon, sodium hexametaphosphate or tripolyphosphate	2·0gm
Metol	6·0gm
Sodium sulphite, anhydrous	50·0gm
Sodium carbonate, anhydrous	30·0gm
Hydroquinone	6·0gm
Potassium bromide	2·0gm
Sodium thiocyanate	1·3gm
Sodium hydroxide, pellets	2·0gm
Potassium iodide, 0·1% solution	6·0ml
Water to	1000·0ml

Stop baths (pH: 3·4–3·6)

Sodium acetate, crystalline	5·3gm
Acetic acid, 98–100% glacial	32·0ml
Water to	1000·0ml

Colour developer (pH: 11·8–12·0)

Trisodium phosphate, crystalline, 12H$_2$O	40·0gm

Sodium hydroxide, pellets	8·0gm
Ethylenediamine, 80% solution	3·8ml
or ethylenediamine sulphate, crystalline	7·6gm
Benzyl alcohol, 35% solution*	10·0ml
Tertiary butylaminoborane (TBAB)	0·1gm
Citrazinic acid	1·3gm
EDTA Na4, Celon E, EDTA tetrasodium salt	3·0gm
Sodium sulphite, anhydrous	5·0gm
Potassium bromide	0·2gm
Potassium iodide, 0·1% solution	10·0ml

Add before use:
Kodak CD3 (M & B Mydochrome: Activol No 3)	12·0gm
Water to	1000·0ml

Benzyl alcohol, 35% solution
Benzyl alcohol	35·0ml
Diethylene glycol	45·0ml
Water	20·0ml
	100·0ml

Bleach (also for E3) (pH: 6·6–7·0)
Potassium ferricyanide	112·0gm
Potassium bromide	24·0gm
Disodium phosphate, crystalline, 7H₂O	45·0gm
Monosodium phosphate, anhydrous	12·0gm
Sodium thiocyanate	10·0gm
Water to	1000·0ml

Fixer (also for E3) (pH: 4·5–4·9)
Ammonium thiosulphate, crystalline	120·0gm
Potassium metabisulphite, crystalline	20·0gm
Water to	1000·0ml

Stabiliser (also for E3)
Formaldehyde, 35–40% solution	3·0ml
Wetting agent, 10% solution	10·0ml
Water to	1000·0ml

Notes

A Recommended agitation is continuous for the first 15sec, then 5sec every minute.

B Complete transparency of the film is reached only when it is perfectly dry. It should be noted that it is permissible to *dry off the film temporarily* after completion of Stage 5. The film should then be stored in diffused light or preferably in total darkness until processing is to be completed.

C The pre-hardener chemicals should be dissolved in water at 38–40°C with continuous agitation until solution is complete. At least 10min must be allowed to elapse before use to allow the DMTF to become transformed by hydrolysis into succinicaldehyde, a powerful gelatin tanning agent. The solution becomes effective only after this transformation is complete.

D Should it not be possible to obtain the commercial 80% aqueous solution of ethylenediamine (beware of noxious fumes) for the colour developer, the sulphate, which is easier to handle, may be used. In this case, the pH-value may need to be adjusted by adding a few millilitres of a 10% solution of caustic soda. The TBAB, supplied by Kodak Limited in pellet form, should be crushed in a little water, using a glass rod or small pestle, then the remaining solution added. The TBAB can be dispensed with if the usual procedure of reversal by re-exposure to light is followed (see above). The developer in this form can then also be used for Process E3.

E It should be emphasised that any contamination of one solution by another must absolutely be avoided. As the intermediate washes have been reduced to a strict minimum, all utensils employed in processing must be thoroughly cleansed and dried before being used for a succeeding solution.

F The two stop baths should be kept separate to avoid contamination.

G Time of development in the first developer should be increased in accordance with the use it has had. For 20exp 35mm films, or approximately 37sq ft material per film, the times should be as follows:

1–4 films	6min 15sec
5–7 films	6min 30sec
8–10 films	6min 50sec
11–12 films	7min 30sec

H Prolonging first development to 8min results in a 2X increase in the speeds of Ektachrome-X and High Speed Ektachrome.
(See Forced Development, *Popular Photography*, October 1968.)

Keeping properties and working capacities

Solution	Keeping time	Working capacity per litre			
		135–20	135–36	120	sq ft
Pre-hardener	4 weeks	12	7	8	430
Neutraliser	3 months	12	7	8	430
First developer	3 months	12	7	8	430
Colour developer:					
without CD3	6 weeks	—	—	—	—
with CD3	4 weeks	12	7	8	430
Stop baths	6 months	12	7	8	430
Bleach	6 months	18	10	12	650
Fixer	6 months	12	7	8	430
Stabiliser	6 months	should be used fresh			

2-5 dimethoxy tetrahydro furan is available as Item 2961 in 250ml and 1 litre bottles from Merck via their distributors in Great Britain: Anderman and Company Limited, Battlebridge House, 87-95 Tooley Street, London S.E.1. Tert-butylamino borane complex Item BU 441 is available from Schuchardt GMBH, 8 München 80, Gaisbergstrasse 1-3, West Germany, in 10gm packs at DM 22 (£2.20) and 25gm packs at DM 48 (£4.80), duty unpaid.

3M COLOR SLIDE—Compatible with FERRANIACOLOR* DIA 28, CR 50 and CR 50A

General Instructions pp. 205-6

Formulae

First developer RC131 (pH: 9·5±0·1)

Calgon sodium hexametaphosphate or tripolyphosphate	2·0gm
Sodium sulphite, anhydrous	40·0gm
Phenidone*	0·8gm
Hydroquinone	5·0gm
Borax, crystalline	5·0gm
Potassium bromide	2·5gm
Sodium thiocyanate	0·7gm
Caustic soda, pellets	0·8gm
Water to	1000·0ml

*Dissolve separately in 50ml warm water (80°C) and add to the rest of the solution.

Stop bath VC233 (pH: 4·0±4·5)

Sodium acetate, crystalline	50·0gm
Potassium alum	30·0gm
Sodium or potassium bisulphate	30·0gm
Potassium metabisulphite, crystalline	5·0gm
Water to	1000·0ml

Colour developer RC125 (pH: 11·0–11·2)

Calgon sodium hexametaphosphate or tripolyphosphate	2·0gm
Hydroxylamine hydrochloride (or sulphate 1·2gm)	1·0gm
Sodium carbonate, anhydrous	65·0gm
Sodium sulphite, anhydrous	2·5gm
Potassium bromide	1·2gm
Caustic soda, pellets	0·2–2·0gm*

Add before use:

Ferrania S28, diethyl paraphenylenediamine sulphate	2·8gm
Water to	1000·0ml

*To adjust pH to required value

Bleach-hardener VC212

Potassium ferricyanide	50·0gm
Potassium bromide	25·0gm
Sodium acetate, crystalline	60·0gm
Boric acid	5·0gm
Potassium alum	30·0gm
Water to	1000·0ml

Fixer FC200 (pH: 7–8)

Sodium thiosulphate (hypo), crystalline	200·0gm
Water to	1000·0ml

Stabiliser

Wetting agent, 10% solution	10·0ml
Formaldehyde, 35–40% solution	6·0ml
Water to	1000·0ml

Procedure

1	First developer	14min 20±0·25°C
2	Wash, running water	1min 12–22°C
3	Stop bath	5min 18–22°C
	Normal room lighting may be resumed	
4	Wash	5min 12–22°C
5	Re-exposure, 500W 40in	2×1½min
6	Colour developer	11min 20±0·25°C
7	Wash	1min 12–22°C
8	Stop bath	5min 18–22°C
9	Wash	5min 12–22°C
10	Bleach-hardener	10min 18–22°C
11	Wash	5min 12–22°C
12	Fixer	5min 18–22°C
13	Stabiliser	1min 18–22°C
14	Final wash	15min 12–22°C
15	Wet	½min 18–22°C
16	Dry	— 35°C max
	Total	85½min

*Ferrania official formulae (see Gehret, Ernest—British Journal of Photography, 25 July 1965).

Keeping properties and working capacities

Solution	Keeping time	Working capacity per litre	
		sq ft	120 or 135-20
First developer	3–4 months	3–4	10–12
Stop bath	6–12 months	4–5	10–12
Colour developer:			
without S28	2–3 months	—	—
with S28	1–2 weeks	2–3	5–6
Bleach	6–8 months	4–7	12–18
Fixer	1–6 months	5–7	12–18

Notes

A Recommended agitation during the first 2min in the first developer and colour developer, 5sec every 30sec, then 5sec every minute. For the other baths, 5sec at not less than 30sec intervals.

B Reduction of the time of first and colour development gives a warmer final colour rendering, whereas prolonging it gives a cooler, more blue-violet tone. Very brief washing after colour development gives a warmer colour rendering than a more extended wash.

C Solutions A and B of the colour developer should be prepared separately, then solution A added to solution B, while stirring. As an alternative to the use of Activol S (2·8gm/l), the following may be used:

Activol (Diethyl paraphenylenediamine sulphite) 2·5gm/l—together with a reduction in the quantity of sodium sulphite anhydrous from 2·5 to 1·25gm/l.

Activol H (Diethyl paraphenylenediamine hydrochloride) 2·2gm/l, the weight of sodium sulphite being unchanged.

D Using grades of sodium carbonate supplied for photographic use, the quantity of sodium hydroxide specified (1gm/l) will give a pH-value within the recommended range and results will be entirely satisfactory for all normal purposes.

FUJICHROME R100

Introduction

This reversal material, manufactured by the Fuji Film and Photo Company of Tokyo, of speed ASA 100, is becoming known in Europe, where it has been very well received by the amateur. The favourable reviews of the film and the quality of the transparencies which we had had occasion to examine led us to take a closer look at it and study the possibility of user-processing.

The constitution of this colour film is analogous to that of Ektachrome: the couplers are dispersed in the emulsion by means of a fine suspension of a synthetic resin in which they are dissolved. Such similarity might well be expected to carry with it an identical, or at least closely related, processing procedure. This supposition proved correct, and we give below details and formulae for a procedure which has come up to our expectations.

The colour rendering of Fujichrome is similar to that of High Speed Ektachrome, that is to say slightly colder than that of Ektachrome-X. Contrast seemed somewhat higher than that of the high-speed version. Definition is excellent and grain is fine—at least as fine as that of Ektachrome-X, despite its higher speed. These opinions, it should be emphasised, are purely personal, but they should not be very far from the scientific truth, assuming proper precautions. In short, we have found the material to be of excellent general quality, such as can justly claim a place of distinction among current materials.

We experimented with two different first developers, with good results. The first is the one which we have already quoted in our Ektachrome E3 processing formulae; the second is the RC131, recommended by Ferrania for developing Ferraniacolor Dia 28 and CR50, and also cine film. We have found, however, that here it is advantageous to increase the pH-value slightly to 10·2 instead of 9·5. If the pH-value is left at 9·5 the image is slightly more magenta, particularly noticeable in the skies.

Procedure

1	First developer	8min	24±0·25°C
2	Rinse, running water	1min	20–24°C
3	Hardener-stop bath	3min	20–24°C
	Normal room lighting may be resumed		
4	Wash, running water	3min	20–24°C
5	Re-exposure, 500W at 1m	2×1min	
6	Colour developer	12min	22–24°C
7	Wash, running water	4min	20–24°C
8	Clear	4min	20–24°C
9	Rinse	1min	20–24°C
10	Bleach	3min	20–24°C
11	Wash, running water	1min	20–24°C
12	Fixer	4min	20–24°C
13	Final wash	8min	20–24°C
14	Stabiliser	1min	20–24°C
15	Dry	—	35°C max
	Total	55min	

General Instructions pp. 205-6

Formulae
First developers
No 1 : E3 (pH : 10·3±0·1)

Calgon, sodium hexametaphosphate or tripolyphosphate	2·0gm
Sodium sulphite, anhydrous	40·0gm
Phenidone	0·5gm
Hydroquinone	6·0gm
Sodium carbonate, anhydrous	40·0gm
Potassium bromide	2·0gm
Sodium thiocyanate	2·0gm
Potassium iodide	0·006gm
	(or 6ml 0·1% solution)
6-nitrobenzimidazole nitrate, 0·2% solution*	10·0ml
Water to	1000·0ml

*Optional

No. 2 modified RC131 (pH : 10·2±0·1)

Calgon, sodium hexametaphosphate or tripolyphosphate	2·0gm
Sodium sulphite, anhydrous	40·0gm
Hydroquinone	5·0gm

Borax, crystalline	5·0gm
Potassium bromide	2·5gm
Sodium thiocyanate	0·7gm
Sodium hydroxide (caustic soda), pellets	3·8gm
Water to	1000·0ml

Stop-hardener (pH : 3·5±0·2)

Chrome alum, crystalline	30·0gm
Water to	1000·0ml

Colour developer (pH : 11·9±0·1)

Calgon, sodium hexametaphosphate or tripolyphosphate	2·0gm
Trisodium phosphate, crystalline, $12H_2O$	40·0gm
Sodium hydroxide, pellets	8·0gm
Sodium sulphite, anhydrous	5·0gm
EDTA Na_4, Celon E	3·0gm
Citrazinic acid	1·3gm
Ethylene diamine sulphate	7·5gm
Benzyl alcohol solution*	10·0ml
Potassium iodide, 0·1% solution	6·0ml
Potassium bromide	0·2gm

Add before use :

Kodak CD3 or M & B Mydochrome	10·0gm
Water to	1000·0ml

Make up as follows :

Benzyl alcohol	35·0ml
Diethylene glycol	45·0ml
Water to	20·0ml

(This solution keeps indefinitely)

Clearing solution (pH : 4·6±0·2)

Potassium metabisulphite, crystalline	30·0gm
Water to	1000·0ml

Bleach (pH : 6·7±0·1)

Potassium ferricyanide	112·0gm
Potassium bromide	24·0gm
Monosodium phosphate, anhydrous	12·0gm
Disodium phosphate, crystalline, $7H_2O$	45·0gm
or $12H_2O$ substance	62·0gm
Sodium thiocyanate	10·0gm
Water to	1000·0ml

Fixer (pH : 4·6±0·2)

Ammonium thiosulphate, crystalline	100·0gm
Potassium metabisulphite, crystalline	10·0gm
Water to	1000·0ml

Stabiliser

Wetting agent, 10% solution	10·0ml
Formaldehyde, 35–40% solution, Formol	2·0ml
Water to	1000·0ml

Keeping properties and working capacities

Solution	Keeping time	Working capacity per litre		
		135–36	120	sq ft
First developer	4 months	6–8	8–10	400–500
Hardener-stop	4 months	12	15	750
Colour developer:				
without CD3	2 months	—	—	—
with CD3	2 weeks	6	8	400
Clearing solution	6 months	12	15	750
Bleach	6 months	10	12	600
Fixer	4 months	10	12	600
Stabiliser	1 year	should be used fresh		

Note that Fujichrome RK cartridges for Instamatic cameras are processed in the same manner.

Notes

A Recommended agitation is continuous during the first 15sec, then 5sec every minute.

B By prolonging first development by 2–3min, the effective speed of the film can be increased by about ½ stop without noticeable effect upon colour rendering.

C Re-exposure is not necessary if the film is dried after completion of Stage 4 with the intention of completing processing at a later date. Once dry, however, the film must be kept in the dark. Colour development may then be delayed for up to 4–6 weeks; in this case, the film is immersed direct in the colour developer: preliminary wetting is not necessary.

ORWOCHROME UT18 and UT21*

Introduction

At photokina 1966, VEB Filmfabrik Wolfen (RDA) announced the marketing of a new material, Orwochrome UT18, designed to replace Orwocolor UT16, which by that time had become rather outdated. Unfortunately, the new film had almost immediately to be withdrawn, since it still exhibited some defects in quality (stability). These teething troubles seem to have been surmounted, and for the 1968 photokina a new film was released under the same designation, together with an announcement of other new emulsions—UT16, UK18 and UT21—which will be progressively introduced on to the market.

These modernised films require a different processing procedure, and the solution formulae have been modified: the first developer utilises Phenidone, with its activating properties similar to those of metol. VEB Filmfabrik Wolfen have not yet divulged the complete formulary or processing procedure, and, for the present at least, processing is restricted to authorised laboratories. However, it is very probable that once the procedure has been through a testing period it will be published, as have been the majority of processing procedures of this firm.

We have had occasion to carry out a series of tests with Orwochrome UT18, and these have permitted us to compile the following procedure which will enable those interested to undertake their own processing of this material. In colour rendering, colour separation and definition it can justly claim a place among high-quality reversal films. Colours are much more saturated and pure than with Orwocolor UT16; contrast is slightly higher and the scale of gradation much longer than those of its predecessor, which was a very close relation of the Agfacolor of the heroic period.

The procedure is in accordance with the manufacturers' instructions. It is interesting to note that the working temperature is 25°C, which is much easier to maintain than the traditional 18°C of the old emulsion. The manufacturers have succeeded in sufficiently hardening the emulsion, which formerly had a reputation for being very susceptible to mechanical damage.

Procedure

1	First developer	10min	25±0·25°C
2	Wash, running water	1min	13–24°C
3	Stop bath	2min	18–24°C
	Normal room lighting may be resumed		
4	Re-exposure, 500W at 1m	2×2½min	
5	Colour developer	12min	25±0·25°C
6	Wash, running water	20min	13–24°C
7	Bleach	5min	18–24°C
8	Wash, running water	5min	13–24°C
9	Fixer	5min	18–24°C
10	Final wash	15min	13–24°C
11	Wet	1min	18–24°C
12	Dry	—	30°C max
	Total	81min	

Gehret, Ernest—The British Journal of Photography, 28 February 1966.

General Instructions pp. 205-6

Formulae

Apart from that for the first developer, all formulae are as specified by the manufacturers.

First developers (or as for E3)
No 1: (pH: 10·2–10·3)

Calgon, sodium hexametaphosphate or tripolyphosphate	2·0gm
Sodium sulphite, anhydrous	40·0gm
Sodium carbonate, anhydrous	34·0gm
Phenidone	0·8gm
Hydroquinone	6·0gm
Potassium bromide	2·5gm
Sodium thiocyanate	1·2gm
Potassium iodide, 0·1% solution	6·0ml
Water to	1000·0ml

No 2: (pH: 10·3±0·1)

Calgon, sodium hexametaphosphate or tripolyphosphate	2·0gm
Sodium sulphite, anhydrous	40·0gm
Sodium metaborate	5·0gm
Phenidone	0·8gm
Hydroquinone	5·0gm
Potassium bromide	2·5gm
Sodium thiocyanate	0·8gm
Potassium iodide, 0·1% solution	6·0ml
Caustic soda, pellets	about 0·8gm*
Water to	1000·0ml

*To adjust pH to required value

Stop bath C37 (pH: 4·2±0·1)

Sodium acetate, crystalline	15·0gm
Acetic acid, 98–100%	25·0gm
Water to	1000·0ml

Bleach bath C57 (reinforced) (pH: 6·2±0·2)

Potassium ferricyanide	100·0gm
Potassium bromide	30·0gm
Monosodium phosphate, anhydrous	5·8gm
Disodium phosphate, crystalline, 12H_2O	4·3gm
Water to	1000·0ml

Colour developer C15 (pH: 10·7±0·2)

Calgon, sodium hexametaphosphate or tripolyphosphate	4·0gm
Hydroxylamine sulphate	1·2gm
Sodium sulphite, anhydrous	2·0gm
Potassium carbonate	75·0gm
6-nitrobenzimidazole nitrate, 0·2% solution	5·5ml
Potassium bromide	2·5gm

Add before use:

Diethyl paraphenylenediamine sulphate	3·0gm
Water to	1000·0ml

Fixer C73 (for quick fixing) (pH: 6·6±0·3)

Sodium tripolyphosphate, crystalline	200·0gm
Ammonium chloride or sulphate	80·0gm
Water to	1000·0ml

Notes

A Recommended agitation is continuous for 2min, then 5sec every minute.

ANSCOCHROME 64
D/200, D/500, T/100*

Introduction
This film is of the usual integral coupler type; comparing it with earlier Anscochrome the improvement in colour rendering is immediately apparent, especially in the reds of the artificial light film T/100. The exposure latitude is very satisfactory, giving good rendering over a range of ±1 stop, but it must be understood that only an absolutely accurate exposure can give the best possible result. Colour balance may be regarded as neutral in comparison with Ektachrome-X, which gives a 'warm' rendering.

Processing, as before, may be carried out by the user with the manufacturers' kits or by the use of appropriate substitute formulae. The formulae already published for Anscochrome may be used but the results are not very satisfactory particularly in as much as the processing temperature now recommended is 80°F (26·7°C) instead of 20°C for the old Anscochrome instructions. This higher temperature has the advantage of reducing the overall processing time from 71–74 to 44½min; on the other hand, it does mean greater care in handling since the resistance of the film to mechanical damage is less at this higher temperature; however, processing does not in fact present any difficulty other than that of maintaining the solutions at the specified temperatures.

The procedure is that recommended by the manufacturers: it applies to all four types. The references are to Ansco solutions.

The formulae given here have, in the author's hands, given results of excellent quality comparable with that obtained with the official kits.

Procedure

1	First developer	504-A	8½min	26·70±0·25°C
2	Hardener-stop bath	907-A	2min	26·70±1°C
3	Wash, running water —		2½min	24–26·7°C
	Normal room lighting may be resumed			
4	Re-exposure	—	2×¼min†	
5	Colour developer	611	10min	26·70±0·25°C
6	Hardener-stop bath	907-A	2min	26·7±1°C
7	Wash	—	5min	24–26·7°C
8	Bleach	718-B	3½min	26·7±1°C
9	Wash	—	2½min	24–26·7°C
10	Fixer	806-A	2½min	26·7±1°C
11	Wash	—	4min	24–26·7°C
12	Stabiliser	955	½min	26·7±1°C
13	Wash	—	½min	24–26·7°C
14	Wet	954-B	½min	26·7±1°C
15	Dry	—	—	38°C max

Total   44½min

General Instructions pp. 205-6

Formulae

First developer (pH: 10·2 ± 0·1)

Metol	2·8gm
Sodium sulphite, anhydrous	50·0gm
Hydroquinone	6·0gm
Sodium metaborate, crystalline	45·0gm
Tri-sodium phosphate, crystalline, 12H$_2$O	4·0gm
Potassium bromide	2·0gm

Potassium iodide	0·01gm
Sodium thiocyanate	2·0gm
6-nitrobenzimidazole nitrate*	0·04gm
Water to	1000·0ml

*Optional

Stop-hardener (pH: 4–4·4)

Sodium acetate, crystalline	20·0gm
Potassium alum	10·0gm
Sodium or potassium bisulphate	12·0gm
Boric acid	3·0gm
Water to	1000·0ml

Colour developer (pH: 10·8±0·1)

Sodium sulphate, anhydrous	100·0gm
Tri-sodium phosphate, crystalline	20·0gm
Sodium metaborate, crystalline, or Kodalk	40·0gm
Sodium sulphite, anhydrous	5·0gm
Potassium bromide	1·0gm
Potassium iodide	0·01gm
β-phenylethylamine (free base)	2·0gm
or its hydrochloride	2·5gm

Add before use:

N-ethyl-N (β-oxyethyl)-paraphenylene-diamine sulphate	5·0gm
Water to	1000·0ml

Bleach (pH: 5·1–5·2)

Potassium ferricyanide	50·0gm
Potassium ferrocyanide	5·0gm
Potassium bromide	15·0gm
Sodium acetate, crystalline	60·0gm
Boric acid, pellets	5·0gm
Potassium alum	30·0gm
Water to	1000·0ml

Fixer (pH: 9·5±0·2)

Sodium thiosulphate, crystalline	150·0gm
Sodium sulphite, anhydrous	10·0gm
Formalin, 35–40% solution	25·0ml
Boric acid, pellets	10·0gm
Water to	1000·0ml

Stabiliser (pH: 5·8±0·2)

EDTA tetrasodium salt (Versene)	2·5gm
Tartaric acid	4·0gm
Sodium metaborate, crystalline	6·0gm
Water to	1000·0ml

Keeping properties and working capacities

Solution	Keeping time	Working capacity per litre 135-36	sq ft
First developer	4 months	6	3·5
Hardener-stop*	4 months	6	3·5
Colour developer:			
without ethyl-oxyethyl ppd sulphate	6 months	—	—
with ethyl-oxyethyl ppd sulphate	2 months	6	3·5
Bleach	6 months	10	5
Fixer	6 months	10	5
Stabiliser	6 months	10	5

*Recommended procedure is to prepare two solutions using one to follow the first developer and the other for the colour developer.

*Gehret, Ernest—The British Journal of Photography, 11 March 1966.

†Stretched the length of a fluorescent tube at a distance of 4–6 ins; or, using a 100W tungsten lamp, two exposures of ½min at 1ft.

For bleaching it is also possible to use one of the formulae given below, both of which are excellent:

Bleach 1, Ferrania VC212 (pH: 5·1–5·6)

Potassium ferricyanide	50·0gm
Potassium bromide	25·0gm
Sodium acetate, crystalline	60·0gm
Boric acid, pellets	5·0gm
Potassium alum	50·0gm
Water to	1000·0ml

Bleach 2 (pH: 5·5–5·8)

Potassium ferricyanide	60·0gm
Potassium bromide	20·0gm
Sodium acetate, crystalline	60·0gm
Potassium alum	10·0gm
Water to	1000·0ml

Notes

A Recommended agitation is for both developers continuous for the first 15sec, then 5sec every 30sec; continuous agitation in the other solutions and washes.

B The manufacturers recommend that washing should not be prolonged beyond the times specified and that the temperature of the wash water should not in any case exceed 26·7°C.

C It is permissible to work at temperatures lower than those specified by the manufacturers, at any rate in the case of solutions other than the developers. However, we do not recommend going below 20–22°C in order to minimise the risk of reticulation. Moreover in working at lower temperatures, times should be increased by about 30% to compensate for the reduction of speed of exchange between the emulsion and the wash water or solutions.

PERUTZCOLOR C18*

Introduction

The first developer formulae have been established both of which have given satisfaction. One is of conventional metol-hydroquinone type, as before; the other is based upon the use of phenylpyrazolidone (Phenidone). The keeping quality of the solution is thereby improved and the colour rendering is slightly warmer.

General Instructions pp. 205-6

Formulae

First developer 1 (pH: 9·8–9·9)

Metol	6·0gm
Sodium sulphite, anhydrous	40·0gm
Hydroquinone	4·0gm
Sodium carbonate, anhydrous	60·0gm
Potassium bromide	2·0gm
Sodium thiocyanate	1·3gm
Potassium iodide	0·02gm
Water to	1000·0ml

First developer 2 (pH: 9·8–9·9)

Sodium sulphite, anhydrous	40·0gm
Phenidone†	0·5gm
Hydroquinone	4·0gm
Sodium carbonate, anhydrous	60·0gm

†Should be dissolved separately in a little warm water and the other chemicals in the order given.

*Gehret, Ernest—The British Journal of Photography, 9 September 1960.

Potassium bromide	2·0gm
Sodium thiocyanate	1·3gm
Potassium iodide	0·02gm
Water to	1000·0ml

Hardening stop bath (pH: 3·4–3·7)

Chrome alum, crystalline	30·0gm
Water to	1000·0ml

Colour developer (pH: 10·7–10·9)

Hydroxylamine hydrochloride	1·5gm
Potassium carbonate	60·0gm
Sodium sulphite	5·0gm
Potassium bromide	0·5gm
Benzyl alcohol or 35% solution of benzyl alcohol	14ml

Add before use:

CD2 (2-amino-5-diethylamino toluene hydrochloride) M & B Tolochrome	3·0gm
Water to	1000·0m

Clearing bath (pH: 4·4–4·6)

Potassium metabisulphite, crystalline	20·0gm
Water to	1000·0ml

Bleach (pH: 8·7–9·2)

Potassium ferricyanide	80·0gm
Potassium bromide	20·0gm
Sodium carbonate, anhydrous	3·0gm
Sodium thiocyanate	10·0gm
Water to	1000·0ml

Fixer (pH: 4·6±0·2)

Ammonium thiosulphate, crystalline	120·0gm
Potassium metabisulphite, crystalline	10·0gm
Water to	1000·0ml

Stabiliser

Formalin, 35–40% solution	6·0ml
Wetting agent, 10% solution	10·0ml
Water to	1000·0ml

Procedure

1	First developer	15–15½min	24±0·25°C
2	Rinse	1min	16–26°C
3	Hardener-stop bath	3min	20–26°C
	Normal room lighting may be resumed		
4	Wash	3min	16–26°C
5	Re-exposure, 500W at 30cm	2×1½min	
6	Colour developer	10min	20–26°C
7	Rinse	5min	16–26°C
8	Clear	5min	20–26°C
9	Rinse	1min	16–26°C
10	Bleach	5min	20–26°C
11	Rinse	1min	16–26°C
12	Fixer	4min	20–26°C
13	Final wash	10min	16–26°C
14	Stabiliser	1min	16–26°C
15	Dry	—	40°C max
	Total	67–67½min	

Keeping properties and working capacities

Solution	Keeping time	Working capacity per litre 135-36	Working capacity per litre sq ft
First developer	3 months	6	$3\frac{1}{2}$–4
Hardener stop	2 months	8	5–$5\frac{1}{2}$
Colour developer:			
without CD2	2–3 months	—	
with CD2	1–2 weeks	6	$3\frac{1}{2}$–4
Clearing bath	6 months	8	5–$5\frac{1}{2}$
Bleach	6 months	10	$6\frac{1}{2}$
Fixer	6 months	8	5–$5\frac{1}{2}$

Notes

A Recommended agitation is continuous for the first 15sec, then 5sec every 30sec.

B Intermediate drying is permissible after Stage 4. In this case, re-exposure occurs naturally. The remaining processing procedure should be carried out within 6 weeks (we ourselves have obtained very good results even after 8 months).

C Stabilising is not essential but is desirable for safety's sake.

D To assist accurate compounding of the first developer, it is helpful to make up 10 or 20% solutions of potassium bromide and sodium thiocyanate, and a 1% solution of potassium iodide, from which the requisite quantities are added by pipette.

E The benzyl alcohol for the colour developer can be added as 5ml of the pure substance but difficulty may be experienced in dissolving it: it is therefore preferable to employ it in the form of a 35% solution in a mutual solvent:

Benzyl alcohol	35·0ml
Diethyleneglycol	45·0ml
Water to	20·0ml
	100·0ml

F Increasing the proportion of hydroquinone in the first developer in relation to metol increases general contrast and *vice versa.* However, the Phenidone formula would appear to us to be preferable. As regards the *sodium thiocyanate,* any increase in concentration beyond 1·30gm/l gives a slight increase in film speed by with a cyan colour cast (through its effects on the layer containing the yellow coupler). However, good results have been obtained with 2gm/l thiocyanate provided the first development is curtailed to 12–13min. The alkalinity of the colour developer is a determining factor in maintaining colour equilibrium: if the pH-value is higher than that prescribed, there is a tendency to a green cast; a lower pH-value gives slightly warm transparencies, but the developer activity is greatly reduced below a pH-value of 10·5.

NEGATIVE–POSITIVE COLOUR PROCESSING

KODACOLOR-X and EKTACOLOR PROFESSIONAL L and S*

Introduction

In view of the interest shown by amateurs in Ektacolor paper, on which prints can be made from Kodacolor-X and Ektacolor negatives, the author published* processing procedures for these colour negative materials which need substantially different treatment to colour negative materials of European origin.

Kodacolor-X and Ektacolor Professional can be processed in the same solutions and the procedure is identical. The result is a colour negative in complementary colours with automatic generation of colour coupler masks in the magenta and cyan dye layers.

*Gehret, Ernest—The British Journal of Photography, *13 February 1959* and *15 July 1960.*

General Instructions pp. 205-6

Formulae

Colour developer (pH: 10·5–10·6)

Calgon:	2.0gm
Benzyl alcohol	8·5ml
Sodium metaborate, crystalline, or Kodalk	35·0gm
Trisodium phosphate, crystalline	25·0gm
Sodium sulphite, anhydrous	2·5gm
Potassium bromide	1·5gm
Potassium iodide	0·006gm
CD3	7·8gm
Water to	1000·0ml

Stop bath (pH: 4·3–4·7)

Glacial acetic acid	20·0ml
Sodium sulphite, anhydrous	10·0gm
Water to	1000·0ml

Hardener (pH: 10·4–10·8)

Formalin, 35–40% solution	20·0ml
Sodium carbonate, anhydrous	10·0gm
Water to	1000·0ml

Bleach (pH: 6·6–7·0) (See also formula for E3/E4 bleach, which acts faster)

Potassium nitrate, crystalline	25·0gm
Potassium ferricyanide	20·0gm
Potassium bromide	8·0gm
Boric acid	5·0gm
Borax, crystalline	1·0gm
Water to	1000·0ml

Fixer (pH: 4·4–4·6)

Ammonium thiosulphate, crystalline	120·0gm
Potassium metabisulphite	20·0gm
Water to	1000·0ml

Keeping properties and working capacities

Solution	Keeping time	Working capacity per litre		
		Roll films (120 or 620)	35mm (20 exp)	Sheet film 4×5in
Colour developer:				
with CD3	2 weeks	6–8	8–10	25
without CD3	6 months	6–8	8–10	25
Stop bath	indefinite	6–8	8–10	25
Hardener	1 year	12–16	16–20	50
Bleach	6 months	12–16	16–20	50
Fixer	6 months	12–16	16–20	50

Processing
The several stages are those specified by Kodak:

1	Colour developer	14min 75±0·5°F
2	Stop bath	4min 68–76°F
3	Hardener	4min 68–76°F
	Normal room lighting may be resumed	
4	Wash	4min 68–76°F
5	Bleach	6min 68–76°F
6	Wash	4min 68–76°F
7	Fixer	8min 68–76°F
8	Final wash	8min 68–76°F
	Total	52min

Working capacities for Ektacolor Professional sheet film processing

Solution	Working capacity per litre
	4×5in
Colour developer	15–18
Stop bath	15–18
Hardener	30–36
Bleach	30–36
Fixer	30–36

Notes

A Recommended agitation is continuous for the first 15sec, then 5sec every minute.

B For electronic flash exposures, it was established that the colour characteristics of the negative are often improved by increasing the development time by 2min to 16min for Kodacolor and for Ektacolor S. (Ektacolor L is not in any case suited to this kind of lighting.)

C Films are transferred from the colour developer direct to the stop bath, taking care to carry as little developer over as possible. However, it was confirmed that a brief rinse (20sec) does no harm and extends the life of the stop bath. The same applies to transferring the film from the stop bath to the hardener.

D For sheet films after every three 4×5in films the time of development should be increased by 35–45sec. For example:

Film number:	1–3	4–6	7–9	10–12	etc
Minutes:	14	14¾	15½	16¼	etc

For maximum uniformity of results it is advisable to develop at least 2–9 films together (by the use of suitable dishes) and to use considerable quantities—1gal or more—of solution. In this case an increase of developing time will be necessary only every 12–15 4×5in films.

E Here, as in all photographic processing, scrupulous cleanliness throughout is essential. Care should be taken to avoid contamination of one solution by another except in the case of the stop bath and hardener, where as officially prescribed by Kodak the film passes straight from the developer into the stop bath and thence into the hardener without any intermediate rinse. It is, however, as well to drain films before immersing them in that solution. It is in fact possible to increase considerably the life of the stop bath and hardener by giving the film a quick rinse (5sec) in water between solutions. For our part we prefer this method which better conforms with our own niceties of practice.

F The pH-value of the solutions may be adjusted if need be by varying the proportions of the buffer constituents (disodium phosphate, borax, boric acid).

G It is recommended that the CD3 be added immediately before use; this greatly extends the life of the stock solution. A practical procedure is to make up a 20% stock solution of CD3, the requisite quantity being abstracted with a pipette immediately before use:

Potassium metabisulphite	5·0gm
CD3	20·0gm
Water (30°C) to	100·0ml

H By adjusting the proportion of potassium bromide in the colour developer, contrast can be controlled to an appreciable degree. It can be reduced to as little as 1gm/l, which at the same time gives a gain in emulsion speed of about ½ stop but with the risk of increasing colour fog (depending upon the emulsion).

I For roll films and 35mm films the time of development should be increased by 30–45sec for each film developed. Sheet films: the time of development should be increased by 30–45sec for every 5–6, 4×5 films.

EKTACOLOR COMMERCIAL PAPER*

Introduction

Since the previous article on this subject appeared (1966), we have made some modifications and improvements to procedure and formulae with the object of extracting maximum quality from the emulsions currently on the market. Using as a basis the original colour developer, we have made an adjustment to the pH-value, the lower value of which in the old developer gave reduced developer activity (i.e. a lower apparent paper speed). So far as the other solutions are concerned, the changes are of a minor nature; workers now have a choice of three stabiliser baths of equal efficacy, using our bleach-fixer procedure. We have abandoned the practice of colour development at 24°C, for the practical reason that it is too lengthy and because in any case it no longer gives good results with current Ektacolor paper.

We have tested the efficacy of our formulae at high temperatures, that is to say up to 38°C, and details are given below. We have not ourselves used the Kodak Rapid Processor, but would assume that our formulae can be used with it if solutions are diluted (to a degree which we have not yet determined) in order to compensate for the use of continuous agitation (with the exception of the stabiliser-hardener, which probably should be used at the original concentration, or even at greater strength, to compensate for the greater mechanical strain).

On the other hand, the solutions which follow the colour developer may be used at a temperature lower than 30°C, which, incidentally, obviously simplifies things since it means there is practically no need to bother about the temperature of the solutions.

		Procedure 1	Procedure 2
1	Colour developer	7min 30±0·25°C	7min 30±0·25°C
2	Brief rinse	10–20sec 28–32°C	10–20sec 22–26°C (A)
3	Stop-fixer	1min 28–32°C	2min 22–26°C (B)
4	Wash, running water	0·5min 28–32°C	1min 22–26°C
5	Bleach-fixer	2min 28–32°C	3min 22–26°C
6	Wash, running water	4min 23–32°C	8min 22–26°C
7	Stabilisr-hardener	2min 28–32°C	3min 22–26°C (C)
8	Brief rinse	10sec 28–32°C	10sec 22–26°C
9	Dry	— 80° max	— 80° max
	Total	17min	24½min

General Instructions pp. 205-6

Formulae

Adjust with caustic soda

Colour developer (pH: 10·2±10·3)

Sodium metaborate or Kodalk	25·0gm
Sodium sulphite, anhydrous	2·0gm
Hydroxylamine sulphate or hydrochloride	2·0gm
Potassium bromide	0·5gm
Caustic soda, pellets	3·4gm
Benzyl alcohol solution*	45·0ml

Add before use:

Kodak CD3 (M & B Mydochrome, Johnson Activol-3)	8·0gm
or 20% solution†	40·0ml
Water to	1000·0ml

*Make up as follows:

Benzyl alcohol	35·0ml
Diethylene glycol	45·0ml
Water to	100·0ml
(This solution keeps indefinitely)	

†Make up as follows:

CD3	20·0gm
Potassium metabisulphite	2·0gm
Water to	100·0ml
(This solution keeps 3–4 months in a well filled dark bottle)	

Stop-fixer (pH: 4·5±0·2)

Ammonium thiosulphate (or the corresponding quantity of a commercial solution, in general 60%)	120·0gm
Potassium metabisulphite, crystalline	20·0gm
Acetic acid, glacial	10·0ml
Water to	1000·0ml

Bleach-fixer (pH: 6·7±0·1)

Sequestrene NaFe (Geigy)	50·0gm
EDTA tetrasodium salt, 90%	5·0gm
Sodium carbonate, anhydrous	0·5–1·0gm*
Sodium sulphite, anhydrous	10·0gm
Potassium or sodium thiocyanate, 20% solution	50·0ml
Potassium iodide	1·0gm
Ammonium thiosulphate	120·0gm
Water to	1000·0ml

*As required to adjust pH-value to within permissible range.

Stabiliser (pH: 6·5±0·3)

One of the three following alternatives:

	1	2	3
Uvitex CF, PRS Ciba-Greigy or equivalent product	4·0	4·0	4·0gm*
Monosodium phosphate, anhydrous	6·0	—	—gm
Disodium phosphate, crystalline, 7H₂O	1·5	—	—gm
EDTA tetrasodium salt, 90% solution	2·0	6·0	2·0gm
Sodium metaborate	—	7·5	—gm
Tartaric acid	—	5·0	2·0gm
Formaldehyde, 35–40% solution	30·0	30·0	30·0ml

*The addition of an optical whitening agent is not essential but helps to provide purer whites when prints are examined in daylight.

*Gehret, Ernest—The British Journal of Photography, 27 September 1968.

Diethylene (or propylene) glycol	20·0	20·0	20·0ml
Sodium acetate, crystalline	—	—	5·0gm
Water to	1000·0	1000·0	1000·0ml

Keeping properties and working capacities

Solution	Keeping time	Working capacity per litre	
		sq ft	8×10in
Colour developer;			
stock solution	6 months	—	—
working solution	3 weeks	3– 4	6– 8
Stop-fixer	6 months	8–10	16–20
Bleach-fixer	6 months	10–15	20–30
Stabiliser	8 months	9–12	18–24

Notes on development at high temperatures

A   Ektacolor Commercial paper can be processed at temperatures up to 38°C. This permits the total processing time to be notably reduced. However, it is difficult, with a non-mechanised installation, to work under these conditions, but it is nevertheless interesting, in our opinion, to be able to raise somewhat the temperature of the colour developer, thereby shortening the time of processing under darkroom conditions. We have not been able to establish any variation in colour balance or image density as a result of following this procedure. Since the amateur will rarely have a thermostatic installation at his disposal the inevitable fluctuations in temperature of his solutions are not so serious with the shorter times.

B   In order to exploit to the full the capacity of the colour developer, we have adopted the following procedure: 3 litres solution are prepared and in this are developed simultaneously four 8×10in sheets, introduced (and ultimately removed) successively at 15sec intervals, into a 12×16in dish. The first 12 sheets (i.e. three sets of four sheets) are developed for 7min at 30°C and the remainder as follows:

4th set—sheets 13–16:	7min 20sec
5th set—sheets 17–20:	7min 40sec
6th set—sheets 21–24:	8min 00sec
7th set—sheets 25–28:	8min 30sec

The developer is then thrown away. If, however, it should happen that a batch of developer has not been used to its full capacity, 2 litres of it should be kept and stored in a well sealed bottle, where it will keep for, at most, 2 weeks. This should be replenished before use with 1 litre fresh developer and continued to be used until the full number of prints has been developed. If the specfiied total is still not reached, the procedure should be: 2 litres kept and replenished with 1 litre. Larger prints are treated in the same way, keeping, of course, to the same total print area.

C   To facilitate storage, stock solutions can be made up in concentrated form and diluted at the time of use; this reduces the frequency with which solutions have to be made up, with the attendant weighing out operation:

	Concentration	Dilution
Colour developer, without benzyl alcohol or CD3 (both of which are added before use)	4×	1 +3
Stop-fixer	4×	1 +3
Bleach-fixer	2×	1 +1
Stabiliser-hardener	7×	1 +6

Notes

A   Recommended agitation in the colour developer is continuous for the first 10sec, then 5sec each minute. If a number of prints are developed simultaneously in the same dish, the bottom print should be brought to the top of the pile each minute. In the other baths, *at least* the same degree of agitation should be maintained.

B   In order to conserve the stop-fixer solution, we have intercalated here a brief rinse of 10–20sec in water to which has been added 10ml/l acetic acid.

C   If prints are to be glazed or heat dried, the time of treatment in this bath should be doubled.

D   The time of treatment, in each case, includes 10–20sec drainage, depending upon format, before transfer to the next bath.

E   If the temperature of the wash water (and of the other solutions) is lower than that prescribed, it will be necessary to prolong the time of treatment. At 18–20°C double that for 23–35°C must be given.

F   Kodak Limited recommend the addition of their brightening additive to the Ektaprint C stabiliser in order to improve the stability to light of the finished prints. It should, however, be noted that the stability is already excellent without special treatment thanks to the constitution of the emulsion and the couplers. It is further improved by the application of one of their print lacquers (clear or matte).

THE AGFACOLOR NEGATIVE-POSITIVE SYSTEM
AGFACOLOR CNS

Introduction

This material has replaced Agfacolor CN17 Special, production of which had been suspended. Like the earlier material, it incorporates two masks designed to improve colour separation by correcting the unwanted absorptions of the magenta and cyan images. Various improvements in manufacture of the emulsion have enabled Agfa-Gevaert to put on the market a film rated at ASA 80 of very fine grain and improved resolution (110lp/mm for the yellow layer, 65lp/mm for the magenta and 45lp/mm for the cyan layer are quoted by the manufacturers).

Agfacolor CNS is supplied in the usual 'amateur sizes': 120/620, 35mm (20- and 36-exposure and 30m rolls) and 126 cartridges for 12 and 20 exposures. It is balanced for daylight (approximately 5500°K), xenon lamps or electronic flash. If used in tungsten light, the appropriate filters should be employed.

Professional films corresponding to Agfacolor 80S and 80L Professional will be available shortly.

Construction

Agfacolor CNS has a total emulsion thickness of about 25μ. The order of the coatings, from the base outwards, is as follows, ignoring the (colourless) coatings separating the individual layers:

Base.

Red-sensitive layer (comprising two component layers) in which is formed the cyan dye and the complementary red mask.

Green-sensitive layer; this is actually a multiple coating, for it contains, in the lowermost coating, a colour former for the yellow mask, superimposed by two layers in which will be formed the magenta dye.

A layer containing a yellow filter, which disappears in course of processing.

Blue-sensitive layer in which is formed the yellow dye.

Mask formation

The two masks are each formed in a special way, which differs from the coloured coupler process employed by, among others, Kodak, 3M, Orwo and Fuji.

The red mask of the cyan layer is formed in the bleach bath by oxidation coupling of the residual coupler (which has not reacted during colour development) with an auxiliary mask-forming substance incorporated in this layer of the emulsion. (The process is the same as that which characterised the old Gevacolor Mask, where the mask formed was an alkyl derivative of 3-aminoguanidine.)

The yellow mask former (which is actually a slightly yellow-tinted coupler) is transformed into a colourless derivative in those parts of the image where the magenta dye is formed in direct proportion to the amount of magenta dye (by coupling of the oxidation product with the colour former). The residual yellowish coupler is transformed into a definite yellow mask by oxidation in the bleach bath.

Comparative colour rendering and quality

Prints made from a double-masked negative, when compared with those from an unmasked negative, shows a very decided improvement in general colour rendering: yellow is more saturated, blue is more luminous, green is purer and less blue, magenta is more bluish and less intense, red is more saturated and cyan is greener and more luminous. The grain is relatively fine; definition is sufficiently good easily to permit enlargements of 12-14 diameters (30×40cm from a 24×36mm negative). The exposure latitude is sufficient to give good-quality images over a range of —1 to +2 stops, equivalent to a range of speed ratings from ASA 20 to 160.

Procedure (as specfied by Agfa)

1	Colour developer	8min 20±0·2°C
2	Intermediate bath	4min 20±0·2°C
3	Wash, running water	15min 14–20°C
4	Bleach	5min 20±0·5°C

Normal room lighting may be resumed (actually after 1min in previous bath)

5	Wash, running water	5min 14–20°C
6	Fixer	5min 18–20°C
7	Final wash	10min 14–20°C
8	Wetting agent	½min 14–20°C
	Total	52½min

General Instructions pp. 205-6

Formulae

Colour developer (pH: 11·0–11·3)

Calgon, sodium hexametaphosphate or tripolyphosphate	2·0gm
Hydroxylamine hydrochloride or sulphate	1·4gm
Sodium sulphite, anhydrous	2·0gm
Potassium carbonate	75·0gm
Potassium bromide	2·5gm

Add, some hours before use:

Diethyl paraphenylenediamine sulphate	5·0gm
Water to	1000·0ml

Intermediate bath (pH: 10·2–10·5)

Magnesium sulphate, crystalline	30·0gm
Colour developer, used	30·0ml
Water to	1000·0ml

Bleach (pH: 5·8–6·2 (critical!))

Potassium ferrocyanide	5·0gm
Potassium ferricyanide	20·0gm
Potassium bromide	12·0gm
Monosodium phosphate, anhydrous	7·0gm
Disodium phosphate, crystalline, $7H_2O$	2·0gm
Water to	1000·0ml

Fixer (pH: 8·0–9·0)

Sodium sulphite, anhydrous	10·0gm
Sodium thiosulphate, crystalline	200·0gm
Water to	1000·0ml

Keeping properties and working capacities

Solution	Keeping time	Working capacity per litre		
		135–36	120/620	sq ft
Colour developer:				
without diethyl ppd	4 months	—	—	—
Complete*	2 weeks	4–5	5	2½
Intermediate bath		should be used fresh		
Bleach	4–6 months	8	10	5
Fixer	4 months	6	8	4
Wetting agent	1 year	should be used fresh		

*To ensure greater uniformity in negative characteristics, we advise using fresh colour developer every time.

Notes

A Recommended agitation is continuous for the first 15sec, then 5sec twice a minute.

B Any increase in treatment time or excessive agitation in the bleach (Step 4) may result in the formation of a too dense mask. In our opinion, it is preferable to give 5sec agitation only once a minute in this bath and (from our own experience) to cut the time to 4min.

C Depending upon the contrast required, development may be for 7–9min.

D Diethyl paraphenylenediamine sulphate has an annoying tendency to form oily droplets of the free base when dissolved in the remainder of the colour developer. It is of advantage to dissolve it separately in 20ml pure water and add this solution with continuous agitation. It is also possible to prepare a 20% stock solution, measuring off the requisite quantity as required:

Diethyl paraphenylene diamine sulphate	20·0gm
Potassium metabisulphite	2·0gm
Water to	100·0ml

This solution keeps for 2–3 months in a well sealed bottle in the dark.

AGFACOLOR CN17 UNIVERSAL

This non-masked material is likewise available in the usual sizes and is processed in the same manner and with the same solutions as Agfacolor CNS.

AGFACOLOR PAPER MCN111 TYPE 7

Introduction

The characteristics of this colour paper have been adapted to the presence of the masks in Agfacolor CNS. The sensitivities of the three layers have been greatly increased in comparison with those of the CN111 paper for non-masked negatives: 10 times for blue, about $2\frac{1}{2}$ times for green and 3 times for red. The overall gain in speed is about $3\frac{1}{2}$ times. Moreover, the colour separation is greatly improved: overlapping of colour sensitivities has been substantially reduced (and, in fact, completely eliminated between green and red).

The contrast of the new Type 7 paper is very slightly higher than that of CN111 (gamma 2·3 as against 2·0), which to some extent compensates for the lower contrast of the CNS negative. The order in which the layers are coated is the reverse of that of the CN111 paper:

CN111	MCN111/7
cyan	yellow
magenta	magenta
yellow	cyan
base (baryta-coated paper)	base (baryta-coated paper)

The manufacturers recommend that the paper should if possible be stored at a temperature below 10°C (in a refrigerator) and that the relative humidity should not exceed 60%. In view of the high sensitivity of the paper, it should not be exposed for more than 2min to the light of an Agfa-Gevaert 08 safelight, using a 15W lamp at a minimum distance of 30in.

The colour rendering of MCN111 Type 7 paper is, subjectively speaking, perfect; all the colours are rendered with a brilliance and purity which it would be difficult to improve upon, and the (border) whites are practically free from fog. The prints can be glazed without difficulty cold or in a heated press at a maximum temperature of 80°C.

Procedure (Agfa recommendation)

Depending upon facilities, it is possible to work at 20 or 25°C, processing time being considerably reduced at the higher temperature.

		20°C procedure	25°C procedure
1	Colour developer	5min 20±0·5°C	3min 25±0·3°C
2	Rapid rinse	$2\frac{1}{2}$min 14–20°C	$1\frac{3}{4}$min 14–20°C
3	Stop-fixer	5min 18–20°C	$1\frac{3}{4}$min 18–25°C

Normal room lighting may be resumed (actually after 1–2min in previous bath)

4	Bleach-fixer	5min 18–20°C	$3\frac{1}{2}$min 23–25°C
5	Wash, running water	10min 14–20°C	$5\frac{1}{4}$min 14–20°C
6	Stabiliser	$2\frac{1}{2}$min 18–20°C	$1\frac{3}{4}$min 18–25°C
	Total	30min	17min

General Instructions pp. 205-6

Formulae (as specified by Agfa)

The colour developing agent recommended by the manufacturers is 4-(N-ω-sulpho-n-butyl-N-n-butylamino)-aniline (Ac 60). This substance is not commercially available but may be substituted by hydroxyethylethyl paraphenylenediamine (sulphate) sold under the names:

> Droxychrome (May & Baker)
> Activol 8 (Johnsons of Hendon)
> S5 (Ansco)
> T32 (Orwo)

Kodak CD3 (M & B Mydochrome, Merck Colour Developer 3) may also be used provided it is added in the form of a 10–20% solution. The use of one or other of these agents requires slight modification of filter values and it is advisable to prolong development by $\frac{1}{2}$–1min (at 20°C) (20–35sec at 25°C). Diethylparaphenylenediamine sulphate is also very suitable and gives results which are close to those obtained with Ac 60, without modification of the developing time.

Colour developer (pH: 10·8–11·0)

Calgon, sodium hexametaphosphate or tripolyphosphate	2·0gm
Hydroxylamine sulphate	4·0gm
Sodium sulphite, anhydrous	4·0gm
Potassium bromide	1·0gm
Potassium carbonate	100·0gm

Add, some hours before use:

Ac 60 (Agfa) or	6·5gm
T32/Droxychrome/S5 or	7·5gm
CD3/Mydochrome	10·0gm
or diethyl paraphenylene diamine sulphate	4·0gm
Water to	1000·0ml

Stop-fixer (pH: 7·1–7·3)

Calgon, sodium hexametaphosphate or tripolyphosphate	2·0gm
Borax, crystalline	30·0gm
Monopotassium phosphate, anhydrous	25·0gm
Sodium sulphite, anhydrous	8·0gm
Thiosemicarbazide*	2·0gm
Sodium benzylsulphinate*	0·5gm
Sodium thiosulphate, crystalline	200·0gm
Water to	1000·0ml

*See previous note.

Bleach-fixer (pH: 7·4–7·7)

EDTA Na₄, Celon E	25·0gm
Borax, crystalline	30·0gm
Sequestrene NaFe (Geigy)	30·0gm
Monopotassium phosphate, anhydrous	15·0gm
Sodium sulphite, anhydrous	2·0gm

*Provided replenishment of solutions is carried out, these two substances may be omitted.

Thiosemicarbazide*	3·0gm
Sodium benzylsulphinate*	1·5gm
Sodium thiosulphate, crystalline	290·0gm
Water to	1000·0ml

Stabiliser (pH: 6·5–8·0)

Brightening agent	4·0gm
Sodium acetate, crystalline	3·0gm
EDTA Na$_4$	2·0gm
Formaldehyde, 30%	80·0ml
Water to	1000·0ml

Brightening agents: An industrial product such as:
Leucophore B, R (Sandoz)
Blancophore BBU, BUP, BP (Bayer)
Uvitex CF conc, PRS (Ciba)
Tinopal 2B (Geigy)
Photine C, B (Hickson & Welch)
Celumyl B, R, S (Bezons)

Substitute formulae

It is possible to replace the stop-fixer and bleach-fixer solutions by alternative formulae without any sacrifice of quality. These are simpler and therefore easier to prepare, and since they can be used equally well with the majority of current colour papers, this simplification has an obvious advantage:

Stop-fixer (pH: 4·5–4·7)

Sodium thiosulphate, crystalline, or	20·0gm
Ammonium thiosulphate, crystalline	120·0gm
Potassium metabisulphite, crystalline	20·0gm
Acetic acid, glacial	10·0ml
Water to	1000·0ml

The use of ammonium thiosulphate permits of a 50% curtailment of treatment time.

Bleach-fixer (pH: 6·7–7·2)

Sequestrene NaFe (Geigy)	50·0gm
EDTA Na$_4$	5·0gm
Sodium carbonate, anhydrous	1·0gm
Sodium sulphite, anhydrous	10·0gm
Sodium thiocyanate, 20% solution	50·0ml
Potassium iodide	2·0gm
Ammonium thiosulphate, crystalline	120·0gm
Water to	1000·0ml

Here again, the use of ammonium thiosulphate enables the time of treatment to be almost halved (3min at 20°C, 2min at 25°C).

For the rest, we suggest the following modifications in procedure:

1 After colour development, immerse the prints for 10–15sec in a 1% solution of acetic acid instead of rinsing in running water.

2 Rinse the prints for 15sec in running water before passing them into the bleach-fixer.

Keeping properties and working capacities

		Working capacity per litre	
Solution	Keeping time	10×15cm	sq ft
Colour developer: without Ac 60	3 months	—	—
Complete	3–4 weeks	40	6
Stop-fixer	3 months	120	18
Bleach-fixer	3–4 months	120	18
Stabiliser	3 months	120	18

Printing from non-masked negatives

MCN111 can very well be employed for making prints from non-masked negatives (Agfacolor CN17 Universal or the like). Filtration is simplified by using an orange compensating filter (as supplied by Agfa) or a piece of processed unexposed masked negative film.

Notes

A Recommended agitation is continuous for the first 15sec in the colour developer then 5sec 3–4 times per minute for other baths as frequent as possible.

B The times allowed for washing in running water are not critical: they may be safely increased, especially if the working temperature approaches the minimum specified. For our part, we have made a practice of giving a brief rinse (15sec) between the stop-fixer and the bleach-fixer. If our suggested alternative formulae are employed (which incidentally are also valid in principle for other colour papers), this intermediate rinse is essential, since the difference in pH-value in passing from the one solution to the other is relatively large, with consequent risk of altering the pH-value of the bleach-fixer by carry-over from the preceding solution.

AGFACOLOR PAPER CN111

This material is designed for printing from the non-masked Agfacolor CN17. It is processed in the same solutions and by the same procedure as MCN111. We do not recommend its use with masked negatives (very high filtration in the cyan with consequent very long exposures).

3M COLOR PRINT FILM (Ferrania)

Introduction

Since the merger of Ferrania SpA (Milan, Italy) with the 3M Company, there has been no relaxation of research, and quite a long series of still-further-improved photochemical products has been released. Among others, a new masked negative film has been marketed for the negative-positive process. It replaces Ferraniacolor Negative NM64, which presented certain major processing difficulties, in particular with regard to the composition of the bleach/mask-forming bath, which caused the destruction of the silver image, involving a critical pH-value.

The 3M Color Print film is an integrally masked colour negative film based upon the use of coloured couplers, similarly constituted to Kodacolor/Ektacolor. It carries two masks—in the cyan and magenta layers respectively, one red and the other yellow—produced by the portion of the coupler which has not reacted with the colour developing agent. The process of formation of the masks is similar to that of the previously mentioned Kodak products:

Key
AB	coloured coupler (mask) formed by
A	constituent eliminated at the time of formation of dye during development, by scission from
B	the reactive constituent, combining with
C	the oxidised developing agent to form
BC	dye (cyan or magenta).

This material, with a rated speed of ASA 80, is available in 135 and 120 formats. After processing, it has the characteristic appearance of masked films, with an orange-red base. When printed on to a suitable positive material, it gives prints of high colour fidelity and excellent saturation and purity. Contrast is moderate, rather than low, as we have noted in Kodak material, where considerations of colour outweigh those of light and shade.

It is to be noted that, with certain emulsions, we have observed slight peculiarities in the colour balance, with some symptoms of over-filtration (a greenish tinge to the deep browns), which was probably due to the use of a print material (Ektacolor paper) not entirely suited to the negative material. We must, however, point out that this little incident was not repeated on other occasions.

3M Color Print film is processed in the C22 solutions, this constituting a simplification for processing houses. Such a plan seems to be becoming a general tendency when we remember that Fujicolor M100 is processed in practically the same way, as also is Turacolor negative. On the European side, only Orwocolor NC16 and Fomacolor negative are, up to the present, unmasked.

Procedure

1	Colour developer	14min 24±0·25°C
2	Stop bath	4min 22–26°C
3	Hardener	4min 22–26°C
	Normal room lighting may be resumed	
4	Wash, running water	4min 18–24°C
5	Bleach	6min 22–26°C
6	Wash, running water	4min 18–24°C
7	Fixer	4–8min 22–26°C
8	Final wash	8min 18–24°C
9	Wet	1min 18–24°C
10	Dry	— 35°C max
	Total	49–53min

General Instructions pp. 205–6

Formulae

Colour developer (pH: 10·6±0·1)

Calgon, sodium hexametaphosphate or tripolyphosphate	2·0gm
Trisodium phosphate, crystalline, 12H$_2$O	25·0gm
Sodium metaborate, crystalline, or Kodalk	35·0gm
Sodium sulphite, anhydrous	2·0gm
Benzyl alcohol, 35%	15·0ml
Potassium bromide	1·5gm
Potassium iodide, 0·1% solution	5·0ml

Add before use:

Kodak CD3 or M & B Mydochrome	7·8gm
Water to	1000·0ml

35% benzyl alcohol solution

Benzyl alcohol	35·0ml
Diethylene glycol	45·0ml
Water to	100·0ml

Stop bath (pH: 4·5±0·2)

Acetic acid, 100%	20·0ml
Sodium sulphite, anhydrous	10·0ml
Water to	1000·0ml

Hardener (pH: 10·6±0·2)

Formaldehyde, 35–40% solution (formalin)	20·0ml
Sodium carbonate, anhydrous	10·0gm
Water to	1000·0ml

Bleach (pH: 6·7±0·1)

Potassium ferricyanide	112·0gm
Potassium bromide	24·0gm
Monosodium phosphate, anhydrous	12·0gm
Disodium phosphate, crystalline, 7H$_2$O	45·0gm
Sodium thiocyanate	10·0gm
Water to	1000·0ml

Fixer (pH: 4·6±0·2)

Ammonium thiosulphate, crystalline	100·0gm
Potassium metabisulphite	20·0gm
Water to	1000·0ml

Keeping properties and working capacities

		Working capacity per litre		
Solution	Keeping time	135–20	135–36	sq ft 120
Colour developer, without CD3	3 months	—	—	—
with CD3	2 weeks	6	4– 5	2¼–2¾
Stop bath	1 year	9–12	7– 8	3¼–4¼
Hardener	1 year	9–12	6– 7	3¼–4¼
Bleach	6 months	14–16	9–12	5½–6½
Fixer	4 months	12–14	9–10	4¼–5¼
Wetting agent	should be used fresh			

Notes

A Recommended agitation is continuous for the first 15sec, then 5sec every minute. This procedure should be followed in the colour developer. In the other solutions, this should be regarded as a minimum.

B The stop bath should preferably be used fresh, prepared by 1 +9 dilution of a 10× concentrated solution.

C When stainless-steel vessels are used, a corrosion inhibitor, in the form of 25gm/l sodium potassium nitrate, should be added to the bleach solution.

3M-FERRANIA COLOUR PAPER FCO83

Introduction

This new material, balanced for use with the new 3M Color Print film, requires a processing procedure which is fundamentally modified with respect to the old Ferraniacolor papers. The procedure, moreover, has been 'Americanised' and calls for the use of Kodak CD3 as developing agent, which, we may recall, is in fact the monohydrated sesquisulphate of 4-amino-N-ethyl-N-(β-methanesulphonamidoethyl)-m-toluidine. This substance is less active than the usual derivatives such as diethylparaphenylenediamine, but it has the advantage of being almost completely free from any tendency to stimulate allergies in the operator.

The order of the colour layers of FCO83 paper is not inverted, as in Ektacolor Professional; the yellow dye is formed in the top layer, the cyan in the bottom. The emulsion surface has been greatly improved in the matter of resistance to mechanical damage in order to permit of machine processing at high temperature, which is becoming more and more general as it enables processing houses to satisfy the growing demand for paper prints, thanks to the increased speed of production made possible.

The colour rendering of FCO83 measures up to the ever-growing standards demanded by the public and professional: the reds are vivid and clean, the greys neutral, the yellows brilliant and pure, the blues natural and the browns pleasant with a touch of warmth. Residual fog is almost non-existent, resulting in very pure whites. For the rest, the paper is very fast: we have been able to give exposures of 0·7–1·2sec with the Durst 606 (150W) for a 9×13cm print from a 35mm negative of f/5·6 (Janpol-Color lens) with a 10 00 15 filter! There is, of course, a correspondingly increased danger of fog, and we recommend keeping the paper as far away as possible from the safelamp.

These are unofficial formulae, which have not previously been published, but they give results of equal quality.

Procedure (from manufacturer's technical data)

1	Colour developer	5–6min	28±0·25°C
2	Stop-fixer-hardener	3 (3–4)min	28 (24–28)°C
	Normal room lighting may be resumed (actually after 1min in previous bath)		
3	Wash, running water	2 (2–3)min	24–28°C
4	Bleach-fixer	4 (4–5)min	28 (24–28)°C
5	Wash	10 (10–15)min	28 (24–28)°C
6	Stabiliser	2 (2–3)min	28 (24–28)°C
7	Dry	—	80°C max
	Total	26–36min	

General Instructions pp. 205–6

Formulae

Colour developer (pH: 11·2±0·1)

Calgon, sodium hexametaphosphate or tripolyphosphate	2·0gm
Hydroxylamine sulphate	4·0gm
Sodium sulphate, anhydrous	4·0gm
Potassium carbonate	60·0gm
Potassium bromide	0·5gm
Caustic soda, pellets*	6·0–8·0gm
6-nitrobenzimidazole nitrate	0·01gm
Add before use:	
Kodak CD3	8·0gm
Water to	1000·0ml

*To adjust pH-value to within permissible range

Stop-fixer-hardener (pH: 4·3±0·1) (see also alternative formula below)

Ammonium thiosulphate, crystalline	100·0gm
Sodium sulphite, anhydrous	20·0gm
Acetic acid, 100%	30·0ml
Potassium alum	30·0gm
Sodium acetate, crystalline	30·0gm
Water to	1000·0ml

Bleach-fixer (pH: 6·9±0·1—adjust as necessary)

Sequestrene NaFe (Geigy)	50·0gm
EDTA Na$_4$ (Celon E)	5·0gm
Sodium carbonate, anhydrous	3·0gm
Ammonium thiosulphate, crystalline	120·0gm
Sodium thiocyanate	10·0gm
Sodium sulphite, anhydrous	10·0gm
Potassium iodide	1·0gm
Water to	1000·0ml

Stop-fixer-hardener (alternative formula)

Ammonium thiosulphate, crystalline	100·0gm
Potassium metabisulphite	15·0gm
Potassium alum	15·0gm
Acetic acid, 100%	8·0ml
Borax, crystalline	25·0gm
Water to	1000·0ml

Stabiliser (pH: 7·3±0·2—adjust as necessary)

Optical whitening agent	4·0gm
EDTA Na$_4$ (Celon E)	6·0gm
Sodium metaborate, chrystalline, or Kodalk	4·0gm
Tartaric acid	4·0gm
Formaldehyde, 35–40% solution (formalin)	30·0ml
Diethylene glycol or propylene glycol†	40·0ml
Water to	1000·0ml

†This addition is optional: its object is to render the paper sufficiently hygroscopic after drying.

Notes

A Recommended agitation is slow and continuous during colour development; with 5sec agitation 3–4 times per minute, development time is 6min. For the other solutions: continuous agitation for the first minute, then intermittent (5sec 2–3 times per minute). 10–15sec drainage time is included in the treatment times given.

B If the temperature of the solutions (other than RC424) is below 28°C, the treatment time should be increased as indicated by the figures in parentheses.

C Colour development must *not* be carried out *below* 28°C if good results are to be expected. However, we have worked successfully at 30° and 33°C with curtailed development times of 4½–5 and 3¼–3¾min, respectively.

D To prolong the life of the stop-fixer bath, we have personally adopted an intermediate 15sec rinse in water acidified with 20ml acetic acid per litre.

E A short rinse of 10sec is recommended after removing the prints from the stabiliser.

F Prints should not be removed from the solutions during the treatment times.

BLACK AND WHITE PROCESSING
NEGATIVE DEVELOPERS

FINE GRAIN FORMULAE

All the formulae included here will give some refinement of grain over the developers in the other sections at a given exploitation of a film's speed. The actual degree of refinement will closely relate to the film speed reached *vis-a-vis* the normal ASA rating. Any increase in speed will give some increase in grain, although this can be kept to a minimum in carefully balanced formulae. On the other hand true fine grain will only be obtained at some, albeit small, loss of film speed. When maximum sharpness and definition are required, refer to the Acutance Developer Section, this will be at the expense of a slight increase in granularity and some loss of middle-tone gradation.

MEDIUM FINE GRAIN DEVELOPERS
D-76

Metol	2·0gm	(18gr)
Sodium sulphite, anhydrous	100·0gm	(2oz)
Hydroquinone	5·0gm	(44gr)
Borax	2·0gm	(18gr)
Water to	1litre	(20oz)

D-76 *Replenisher*

Metol	3·0gm	(27gr)
Sodium sulphite	100·0gm	(2oz)
Hydroquinone	7·5gm	(66gr)
Borax	20·0gm	(176gr)
Water to	1litre	(20oz)

This developer has come to be taken as a standard against which the granularity, speed, sharpness and definition given by other developers is compared. Thus a formula will be said to give such and such a speed increase or loss, increased or less granularity, or higher acutance than D-76. It is marketed under various brand names such as ID-11, M & B 320, Johnsons Fine Grain, with small formula variations. The use of the replenisher quadruples the life of the developer, which is otherwise about ten films per litre. Use replenisher without dilution to maintain level of solution in tank, discard some solution regularly to maintain quality. Development times are given below. D-76 gives some rise in activity on use and storage; the addition of 14gm/litre (122gr per 20oz) of boric acid crystals provides additional buffering—which will even out its action and give greater contrast control, with a 10–20 per cent increase in developing time. (See also D-76d below.)

Adox M-Q Borax

Metol	2·0gm	(18gr)
Sodium sulphite, anhydrous	80·0gm	(3oz 88gr)

Hydroquinone	4·0gm	(35gr)
Borax	4·0gm	(35gr)
Potassium bromide	0·5gm	(4·5gr)
Water to	1litre	(20oz)

This formula variant of D-76 gives slightly better sharpness with a slower contrast rise. Development times are 10–20 per cent longer. It is closely related to the ASA developer for miniature films, and the Ansco M-Q Borax formula.

For a Phenidone variant of this formula, see FX-3 below.

A Replenisher

Metol	3·0gm	(27gr)
Sodium sulphite, anhydrous	80·0gm	(700gr)
Hydroquinone	5·0gm	(44gr)
Borax	18·0gm	(160gr)
Water to	1litre	(20oz)

Add ½–¾oz of replenisher for each 36 exposures or 120 size roll film developed in one litre or more, discarding some developer if necessary. This maintains quality and developing time.

ID-68 Ilford P-Q Fine Grain Formula

Sodium sulphite	85·0gm	(6oz 350gr)
Hydroquinone	5·0gm	(175gr)
Borax	7·0gm	(245gr)
Boric acid	2·0gm	(70gr)
Phenidone	0·13·0gm	(4·5gr)
Potassium bromide	1·0gm	(35gr)
Water to	1litre	(80oz)

This buffered borax formula gives a marked film speed increase over D-76—about 30–60 per cent, with a minimum increase in granularity, and good sharpness. Times 6–12 minutes at 68°F. The developer, used undiluted, has a minimum change of activity with use.

D-23

Metol	7·5gm	(66gr)
Sodium sulphite, anhydrous	100·0gm	(2oz)
Water to	1litre	(20oz)

Increase development time by 10 per cent after each film, until 8–10 films per litre have been processed. Use of replenisher extends life to 25 rolls per litre.

Replenisher (DK-25R)

Metol	10·0gm	(88gr)

Sodium sulphite, anhydrous	100·0gm	(2oz)
Kodalk	20·0gm	(176gr)
Water to	1litre	(20oz)

Add ½oz (22 ml) for each 36 exposure length or 120 size roll film, discarding some developer if necessary. This amount applies to replenishment of 1litre (35oz) of developer or more. Replenisher identical to that for D-25.

This developer by R. W. Henn and J. I. Crabtree is the simplest medium fine grain formula. In general it gives good sharpness with slight resolution loss on some films; it is softer working than the D-76 type, and may give a faint increase in granularity; film speed very closely approaches normal.

Those workers beginning to weigh and make up their own solutions are recommended to try this formula in use with slow and medium speed films. Diluted 1+3 it resembles the Windisch compensating formula especially recommended for flashbulb work; developing time 20–30 minutes approximately for slow and medium speed films. Use once and discard. With the Metol reduced to 5gm it becomes Ferrania R33.

D-76d, D-76b, Agfa 14, Agfa 15
D-76d is a 'buffered borax' version of D-76 (see also notes to D-76) giving greater contrast control, more consistent results on re-use, with a slight speed loss, and 25–50 per cent time increase. Agfa 14 gives results similar to D-23 with similar times. D-76b is a motion picture and variable density sound track developer giving softer results than D-76 with similar times. Agfa 15 is suitable for some modern films notably the slow and medium speed ones, times 25 per cent less than D-76 or ID-11, times in which are given in manufacturer's data sheets. The use of these formulae has fallen off in recent years, with the exception of perhaps D-76d. (See also the Ilford published P-Q fine grain formula ID-68 for a Phenidone buffered borax developer above.) The Ferrania developer R18 is identical to D-76d.

Quantities in grammes	D-76d	Agfa 14	D-76b	Agfa 15
Metol	2	4·5	2·75	8
Sodium sulphite, anhydrous	100	8·5	100	125
Hydroquinone	5	—	2·75	—
Sodium carbonate, crystalline	—	—	—	31
Borax	8	—	2·5	—
Boric acid	8	—	—	—
Pot. bromide	—	0·5	—	1·5
Water to 1 litre				

VERY FINE GRAIN DEVELOPER—FX-5b
Metol	4·5gm	(40gr)
Sodium sulphite, anhydrous	125·0gm	(2·5oz)
Kodalk (Sodium metaborate)	2·25gm	(20gr)
Sodium bisulphite	1·0gm	(9gr)
Potassium bromide	0·5gm	(4·5gr)
Water to	1litre	(20oz)

Replenisher
Metol	7·0gm	(62gr)
Sodium sulphite, anhydrous	125·0gm	(2·5oz)
Kodalk (Sodium metaborate)	25·0gm	(0·5oz)
Sodium bisulphite	—	—
Potassium bromide	1·0gm	(9gr)
Water to	1litre	(20oz)

Twenty per cent increase after first film until four or five films have been processed per 20oz or 10 per cent increase until eight to ten films have been developed in 40oz. Use replenisher to maintain level of tank until 25 rolls per litre are processed. Visual contrast is lower than the printing contrast. This formula gives true fine grain with good sharpness and the minimum loss of film speed (30–50 per cent) necessary to achieve very fine grain (see also FX-5 below). Results resemble those in the original two-powder pack 'Microdol', found very suitable for Ilford and Adox films amongst others, although it has been replaced in Kodak usage by the new formula Microdol-X, giving improved definition on Kodak films.

Development Times in minutes at 68°F (20°C)
Pan F—10, FP4(MF)—8, FP4(RF)—12, HP3(MF)—15, HP3(RF)—17, HP4(RF)—15, HP4(MF)—13.

THE 'FX' SERIES
The following series of solvent or 'physico-chemical' fine grain formulae were proposed by G. W. Crawley after lengthy research into the development of present-day films. (*B.J.Phot.* 1960, **107**, Dec. 2, 9, 16, 23, 30, and 1961; **108**, Jan. 6, 13, 27). He found that when the third quality of acutance was added to the requirements of minimum granularity and full film speed, changes might be advantageously made to the type of alkalinity and buffer system employed in a developer. Furthermore makes and types of film differed in the alkali-buffer restrainer system required to obtain best definition. FX-3 is the Phenidone variant of the Adox and ASA evolution of D-76 referred to above; FX-4 is a further variant giving higher film speed and more compensation. FX-5 gives very fine grain with the natural concomitant slight speed loss. FX-11 is balanced solely to give the fullest possible speed increase with the minimum granularity increase. FX-19 is a D-23 type formula giving, however, fuller emulsion speed. All modern films may be developed in any of these developers. FX-3 is the more suitable for the very fastest, as it gives the biggest contrast rise on extended development for low brightness range subjects. FX-18 is a P-Q version of D-76 claiming slightly higher resolving power, with a slight reduction in grain and minimal speed increase allowing use at stock strength without speed loss. *N.B. This formula was incorrectly stated in the 1971 Annual.*

Approximate meter settings
FX-5	—30%
FX-18	+30%
FX-19	+30%
FX-3	+30%
FX-4	+60%
FX-7	+60%
FX-11	+80%–100%

These settings relate to the indices for minimum exposure now in common use.

Quantities in grammes	FX-5	FX-19	FX-3	FX-4	FX-11	FX-18
Metol	5	—	—	1·50	—	—
Phenidone	—	0·75	0·25	0·25	0·25	0·10
Hydroquinone	—	7	6	6	5	6
Glycin	—	—	—	—	1·50	—
Sodium sulphite, anhydrous	125	100	75	100	125	100
Borax	3	—	2·5	2·5	2·5	2·5
Kodalk	—	—	—	—	—	—
Sodium bisulphite	—	—	—	—	—	0·35
Boric acid	1·5	—	—	—	—	—
Pot. bromide	0·5	—	1	0·5	0·5	1·6
Water to 1litre						

Dissolve a pinch of the sulphite first, then the metol, next the rest of the sulphite. Always dissolve the hydroquinone with or before the Phenidone, to prevent any temporary oxidation of the latter.

Average Capacity

FX-5 4–5 films per 20oz, 20% increase after each film.
8–10 films per 40oz, 10% increase after each film.
FX-19 5 films per 20oz, 10% increase after each film.
FX-11, FX-3 5–6 films per 20oz, 10% increase after each film.
FX-18 ⎫ 6–8 films per 20oz, 10% increase after second or
FX-4, FX-7 ⎰ third film and the subsequent ones.

N.B.—FX-3 will show a rise in activity on storage and/or re-use similar to D-76.

Development Times in minutes at 68°F (20°C)

Ilford	FX-19	FX-3	FX-4	FX-11	FX-18
Pan-F		4	4		6·5
FP4	as for	5	4·5		9
FP4 (RF)	FX-3	7·5	7		9
HP3 (MF)	but	8	7		8·5
HP3 (RF)	slower	10	9	as for	10
HP4 (RF)	contrast	9	8	FX-3	9
HP4 (MF)	rise	8	7		7·5
Selopan	after	11	10		10
Mark 5		7	6		7

Kodak	FX-19	FX-11 FX-3	FX-5	FX-4	FX-18
Pan-X (MF)		5	8	5	5·5
Pan-X (RF)	as for	6	9	5·5	6
Plus-X Pan (MF)	FX-3	6	11	6	6
Plus-X Pan Prof. (RF)	but slower contrast	7	10	7	7·5
Veri-pan	rise	7	10	7	7·5
Tri-X (MF)	after	7	10	7	8
Tri-X (RF)		9	12	9	10
Royal-X		10–15	Pointless	9–15	15

Changes in Development Times

Make a note of film batch numbers, and when using a new batch, watch for any unusual contrast change and adjust development time in future accordingly. The brief times above (e.g., on Ilford slow materials) will be found most convenient once temperature and agitation is standardised. Alteration of times by ±25 per cent will not affect meter setting in normal work, if required for contrast adjustment. FX-18 times as for D-76 and ID-11.

ACUTANCE FORMULAE
(For maximum sharpness)

Pyrocatechin Surface Developer
Stock A

Pyrocatechin	80·0gm	(354gr)
Sodium sulphite, anhydrous	12·5gm	(55gr)
Water to	1litre	(10oz)

Stock B
Sodium hydroxide 100gm in 1litre, 1oz in 10oz.

Working Solution

Take 25ml of A, 15ml B and make up to 1litre. Develop 15–20 minutes at 68°F according to film type. The developer keeps reasonably in stock, but deteriorates rapidly when mixed. It is used once and then discarded. Specially recommended

by Windisch for Adox films. Emulsion speed approximately doubled.

N.B.—It is best not to make up more of B than will be used rapidly since its activity will decrease with solution of atmospheric CO_2. If possible hold only A as a stock, and add to Sodium hydroxide weighed up and dissolved on the occasion of use. Working concentration is 1·5gm Sodium hydroxide per litre or 13gr per 10oz, this can safely be taken as three pellets per 20oz, or five fair size ones per litre of working developer, of Johnsons Sodium Hydroxide pellets.

The Beutler Developer
Stock A

Metol	10·0gm
Sodium sulphite, anhydrous	50·0gm
Water to	1litre

Stock B

Sodium carbonate, anhydrous	50·0gm
Water to	1litre

Working solution: 1 part A, 1 part B, 8 parts water.
Developing times: 8–15 minutes at 68°F, 20°C.
See notes on making up FX-1 below for further details of preparing concentrated liquid developers.

FX SERIES

The following formulae were proposed by G. W. Crawley after research into the problems involved.

FX-1 is fundamentally a variant of the Beutler formula claiming better contrast control, together with a mechanism to enhance 'adjacency' effects (see introduction to Acutance section); these are also enhanced by the lower concentration of developing agent.

FX-1 High Acutance Developer, speed increase ½–1 stop
Working Solution

Metol	0·5gm
Sodium sulphite, anhydrous	5·0gm
Sodium carbonate, anhydrous	2·5gm
Potassium iodide 0·001% solution	5·0ml
Water to	1000·0ml

Use once and discard. Do not use Calgon, etc.
Metric workers can make 10X concentrates by the method indicated for English system below.

Stock Solutions: do not use Calgon, etc.

A	Metol	22·0gr
	Sodium sulphite, anhydrous	220·0gr
	Potassium iodide solution	0·001% 15·0ml (4·25fl dr.)
	Water to	10·0oz
B	Sodium carbonate, anhydrous	110·0gr
	Water to	10·0oz

Single Solution Concentrate:

Quantities for A and B may be dissolved together in 10oz of water to form a single solution developer, reject for use when discoloured. ½oz of the water may be replaced by isopropyl alcohol (see making up A below).

Making up

A Use water boiled for just three minutes than cooled to about 90°F. Dissolve a pinch of the weighed sulphite before the metol. Filter and bottle. This solution will keep a year unopened or until discoloration begins, a light tint can be ignored. If ½oz of the water is replaced by isopropyl alcohol, keeping qualities are improved and precipitation in extreme cold avoided. (See FX-2, Making up, A, and for general observations on making up concentrated liquid developers.)

B Dissolve in water prepared as for A.

The 0·001 per cent solution of Potassium iodide can be obtained by dissolving 1gm in 1litre of water—4·5gr in 10oz, if 100ml of that solution is diluted to 1litre, then 100ml of this solution again diluted to 1litre will give a 0·001 per cent solution. This keeps for two years at least.

Working Solution—use once and discard.

One part A, one part B, eight parts water. Mix for two minutes and allow to stand to ensure homogeneity.

Development Times for FX-1 and FX-2 at 68°F (20°C) are as follows:

Equipment contrast variations are more obvious in non-solvent developers and these times may need individual adjustment, particularly in FX-2. For future 'Changes in development times', see under that heading in FX series of Fine Grain developers, page 226.

Agfa IFF	13 minutes
Agfa IF (RF)	16 minutes
Agfa IF (MF)	15 minutes
Ilford Pan-F	12 minutes
Ilford FP4 (MF)	13 minutes
Ilford FP4 (RF)	14 minutes
Ilford Selopan	13 minutes
Kodak Pan-X (MF)	13 minutes
Kodak Pan-X (RF)	15 minutes
Kodak Plus-X Pan (MF)	12 minutes
Plus-X Pan Professional	13 minutes
Kodak Verichrome-pan	18 minutes
Rollei 16	15 minutes

Agitation
6–8 spiral twists each minute in small tanks up to 10oz capacity, 10–12 in larger ones. (See also general notes to FX-2.)

General Notes
FX-1 demands well red-corrected coated lenses, precise exposure, and no camera movement; also first-class enlarging lenses. (Under these conditions—see also preceding paper for full description of compatible lens types—highest resolution and definition will be obtained on Kodak Panatomic-X which will then resolve a *B.J.* classified advertisement page 7–8ft from a suitable 50mm lens on the 35mm stock or 8–10ft from a suitable 75–80mm lens on the roll film). If these conditions are not fulfilled the iodide trace is best omitted; its action in enhancing adjacency effects tends also to accentuate lens aberrations, flare, and any camera movement. In this form it acts as simple modified Beutler developer. Tests on a tripod as above at all apertures with and without iodide will show best choice, when big magnification enlargements have to be made.

FX-13 Acutance Developer, ½ stop speed increase
Add to FX-1 working solution (with or without iodide) 40gm/litre (176 grains per 10oz) of anhydrous sodium sulphite. The bare solvent action removes surface flare and image spread. Films faster than Veripan or Selopan show a definition and grain disadvantage over normal solvent developers. A 2 per cent acetic acid bath may sometimes be necessary to remove white scum. Times approximately two-thirds FX-1 and 2 (see above).

FX-2 Acutance Developer, 80% speed increase
Working Solution

Metol	0·25gm
Sodium sulphite, anhydrous	3·5gm
Glycin	0·75gm
Potassium carbonate, crystalline	7·5gm
*Pinacryptol Yellow 1: 2000 solution	3·5ml
Water to	1000·0ml
Do not use Calgon, etc.	

Stock Solutions (see 'making up' below).

A	Metol	11·0gr
	Sodium sulphite, anhydrous	154·0gr
	Glycin	33·0gr
	Water to	5·0oz
B	Potassium carbonate (crystals, not dried)	330gr

C *Pinacryptol Yellow 1: 2000 solution.

Metric users may make up the 20X concentrated stock solutions A and B in the manner described below for the English system.

This dye is available from Edward Gurr Ltd, Upper Richmond Road West, SW14, or Brunnings Ltd., 133 High Holborn, London, W.C.1.

Making Up
Weigh all constituents of A and B and place on plain pieces of paper separately.

A In 4oz of water, boiled for just three minutes, then cooled to about 90°F, dissolve a pinch of the sulphite, next the metol, then the rest of the sulphite and add the glycin. If the glycin remains as a yellowy suspension after three minutes mixing, add a pinch from the weighed carbonate and restir, repeating the operation if it still fails to dissolve. Alternatively replace ½oz of the water by iso-propyl alcohol which will dissolve the glycin. (Iso-propyl alcohol is available without licence on order from any chemist 30p. per 500ml. Its addition also improves keeping qualities and prevents precipitation in extreme cold, and it is used for these purposes in many commercial developers.) Make up to 5oz. Filter and store in filled bottles. This solution should keep a year unopened, but should be rejected when discoloured to a *deep* yellow (glycin developers are usually a golden tint on making up); partly used concentrate should also be rejected when deeply discoloured. Fresh glycin is a reflectant gold yellow in colour. For best keeping, do not aerate whilst mixing and use spotless vessels. Concentrated liquid developers keep indefinitely until oxidation commences, usually from foreign matter in the solution; deterioration then proceeds rapidly once initiated. The use of distilled water is unnecessary; if used, the mixed solution should still be filtered. Do not use Calgon or other sequestering agents in minimum quantity developers.

B Dissolve the crystals (the bulk remaining if any was necessary to dissolve the glycin in A) in 4oz water prepared as for A and make up to 5oz. This solution maintains activity indefinitely in a full bottle but renew after two months if half used for consistent contrast.

C Keeps indefinitely away from strong light. After two years, however, reject as an increase in activity may occur thereafter.

For working solution, take A ½oz, B ½oz, C 17 minims* (1ml) to make 10oz developer. Mix well. Use once and discard.

If this is difficult to measure, take 1oz of stock C and dilute

Development Times
As for FX-1

General Notes
If agitation is reduced to every other minute or third minute with an increase in time up to $\frac{1}{3}$ or $\frac{1}{2}$, negatives of interesting internal gradation and acutance may be obtained; fast films in Group 1 may also be used. Agitation can be abandoned altogether with a further increase in time. Dilution may be doubled or trebled to form stand developers acting over 1–2 hours at room temperature. This developer is more 'pictorial' than FX-1, which is designed for maximum resolution and definition primarily; FX-2 is far less sensitive to flare, and less demanding on apparatus. Crystalline potassium carbonate is available on order at chemists from BDH Ltd., amongst other suppliers.

FX-16 (Grain Effects on High Speed Films)
This developer has been specially designed to produce an obtrusive grain structure on films of ASA 400 and over, whilst retaining excellent contour sharpness. This retention of sharpness assists in preventing the loss of image quality often found where grain texture has been utilised to give a special effect. The formula is related to the above FX-2 Acutance Developer for slow and medium speed films.

FX-16
(50 per cent speed increase)

Metol	0·5gm
Glycin	0·5gm
Sodium sulphite, anhydrous	4·0gm
Sodium carbonate, anhydrous (Vide also Gen. Notes)	50·0gm
*Pinacryptol Yellow 0·05 per cent solution	250·0ml
Water to	1litre

*For Kodak Royal-X Pan 350ml 1 litre.

Making up
Dissolve the solids in half the total quantity of water at around 90°F, 30°C. Add the dye and make up to the total volume. Make up as required. Use within six hours, adding dye just before use. Use once and discard. Pinacryptol Yellow is available from Edward Gurr Ltd, Upper Richmond Road West, SW14, or Brunnings Ltd., 133 High Holborn, London, W.C.1. Pinacryptol Yellow dissolves readily in hot, not quite boiling water. The 0·05 per cent solution—1:2000—keeps indefinitely in a brown bottle away from the light.

Development Times at 68°F (20°C) in minutes

Kodak		Ilford	
Royal-X Pan	20	HP4 (RF)	13
Tri-X (RF)	12	HP4 (MF)	11
Tri-X (MF)	12		

Agfa			
1000 (RF)	18	1000 (35mm)	15

Agitation. Agitation should be thorough, 10secs per min either spiral or inversion.

General Notes
The grain pattern texture produced by FX-16 disturbs resolution of fine detail but sharpness of contours and medium detail is enhanced markedly, hence print impact is excellent. FX-16 is primarily intended as a developer for operators wishing to experiment with grain structure for special effects, but it can also be used with advantage as an 'acutance' developer for fast films when big enlargements are not required. Texture obtrusiveness can be adjusted by varying the negative area used for enlarging, or using different focal length lenses from the same camera position. With slow and medium speed films there is no gain over over FX-2 and 'acutance' developers, and contrast difficulties may occur.

If the carbonate is replaced by 50gm/litre of sodium metaborate or 'Kodalk' a fluffier grain texture is produced. Development times remain the same or slightly shorter.

GENERAL PURPOSE NEGATIVE DEVELOPERS

Although Universal formulae (see page 231) can be used for general purpose negative development, this term is usually applied to formulae unsuitable for development of enlarging papers, etc., in which some attempt has been made to obtain contrast control or some particular advantage or negative quality obtainable by the use of a developing agent of special properties. Such developers do not make use of a 'solvent' effect, and therefore are not classed as fine-grain developers (see Fine-grain Developers), as they do not give the minimum graininess possible at a given film-speed. Best control is obtained when such formulae are buffered against changes in alkalinity, for example, D-61A and DK-50. Both these formulae can be used for Kodak Royal-X Pan, the Universal formulae given earlier may not.

Ilford General Purpose Negative Developer
(free from organic restrainers)

Sodium sulphite, anhydrous	75·0gm	(0·75oz)
Hydroquinone	8·0gm	(35gr)
Sodium carbonate, anhydrous	37·5gm	(164gr)
Phenidone	0·25gm	(1·1gr)
Potassium bromide	0·5gm	(2·2gr)
Water to	1000·0ml	(10oz)

This concentrated developer is diluted as follows:
For Dish development of plates and films: 1 +2 water.
Developing time: 4 minutes.
For Tank development: 1 +5 water.
Developing time: 8 minutes.
Development temperature: 68°F, 20°C.

Kodak General Purpose Negative Developers

Dissolve chemicals in this order	D-61A	DK-50
Metol	3·1gm (110gr)	2·5gm (11gr)
Sodium sulphite, anhydrous	90·0gm (7oz 90gr)	30·0gm (132gr)
Sodium bisulphite	2·1gm (75gr)	— —
Hydroquinone	5·9gm (210gr)	2·5gm (11gr)
Sodium carbonate, anhdrous	11·5gm (400gr)	— —
Kodalk (Sodium metaborate)	— —	10·0gm (44gr)
Potassium bromide	1·7gm (60gr)	0·5gm (2gr)
Water to	1litre (80oz)	1litre (10oz)

These buffered developers are recommended for development of medium to highest speed roll film, sheet film, and plates. D-61A is used in the dish at 1 +1 dilution or in tanks at 1 +3. Development times for 1 +3, between five and ten minutes at 68°F. DK-50 is normally used as recommended by Kodak at full strength. A diluted form of this developer has been proposed independently as giving a useful balance of natural acutance, gradation and speed qualities with controlled contrast rise, this can be made up as follows:

Diluted DK-50
Film Speed Normal, good sharpness
Working Solution

Metol	0·5gm
Sodium sulphite, anhydrous	6·0gm
Hydroquinone	0·5gm
Kodalk (Sodium metaborate)	10·0×3gm
Potassium bromide	0·125gm
Water to	1000·0ml

Stock Solutions. Calgon may be used.
A Make up DK-50 from the published formula (see above) or from the packed powder as directed on the container.
B Dissolve 1oz Kodalk in 12oz boiled and cooled water.
For working solutions use two parts **A**, one part **B**, seven parts water. Use once and discard.

Development Times at 68°F (20°C)

FP4 (MF)	8min
FP4 (RF)	9min
Plus-X, Selopan,	11min
Pan-X (MF)	10min
Pan-X (RF), Mark 5 (MF)	12min
HP4 (MF), Plus-X Pan (MF)	12min
Prof. (RF)	13min
Veripan, HP4 (RF)	14min
Tri-X (RF)	13min
Royal-X Pan	15–20min according to
Agfa 1000 (MF, RF)	15–20min contrast required

MANUFACTURERS' PUBLISHED FORMULAE FOR SPECIFIC PURPOSES

	D-19b	D-158	D-163	DK-50	ID-2	ID-62	ID-20	
Metol	2·2	3·2	2·2	2·5	2	—	3	gm
Hydroquinone	8·8	13·3	17	2·5	8	12	12	gm
Phenidone	—	—	—	—	—	0·5	—	gm
Sodium sulphite anhydrous	72	50	75	30	75	50	50	gm
Sodium carbonate, anhydrous	48	69	65	—	37	60	60	gm
Kodalk	—	—	—	10	—	—	—	gm
Ilford IBT Restrainer solution	—	—	—	—	—	20	—	ml
Pot. bromide	4	0·9	2·8	0·5	2	2	4	gm
Water to	1	1	1	1	1	1	1	litre

D-19b (Kodak).—A high contrast developer for X-ray and aero films, also useful for general industrial photography. Used undiluted at 68°F, the average time for tank development is five minutes. Suitable also for photo-mechanical and document materials. A well balanced developer of good keeping properties.

D-158 (Kodak).—Primarily the developer for 'Velox' paper. Recommended by Kodak Ltd., as a developer for photomechanical and document copying materials. Dilute 1:1 for use with above materials.

D-163 (Kodak).—Mainly a bromide and chlorobromide paper developer. For papers and lantern plates it is used diluted 1:1, 1:2 or 1:3 according to the brilliance of contrast required, development times being 1½ to 2 minutes at 68°F. Useful also as a negative developer diluted 1:3, giving good contrast and brilliance. Develop 4-6 minutes in a dish and 5-8 minutes in a tank at 68°F, 20°C.

DK-50 (Kodak).—A normal contrast developer suitable for all types of plates and films but specifically recommended for Royal-X Pan film. Particularly suitable for commercial and engineering subjects. Clean working and fog free, giving excellent gradation on super-speed plates and films. The presence of 'Kodalk' as the alkali prevents hot weather blistering of the emulsion in the acid fixing bath. Use without dilution.

ID-2 (Ilford).—The standard M-Q developer for films and plates, and a non-caustic developer for high contrast graphic arts films and plates. For normal use dilute 1:2 dish and 1:5 tank. For line and screen work use at stock solution strength.

ID-62 (Ilford).—A general purpose Phenidone-hydroquinone formula for films, plates, and papers. For films and plates dilute 1:3 dish and 1:7 tank. For contact papers, contact and special lantern plates dilute 1:1. For enlarging papers dilute 1:3.

ID-20 (Ilford).—A Pehnidone-hydroquinone or metol-hydroquinone developer for all types of enlarging papers and specially recommended for Ilford, Bromide, Plastika, and Multi-grade papers. For use it is diluted 1:3, development time 1½–2 minutes at 68°F. With bromide paper the development time may be reduced to 1–1½ minutes with double strength developer.

The formula of ID-20 P-Q is not published: the formula above being for ID-20 M-Q.

PROCESS DEVELOPERS
These are used for copying and process materials, graticules, photomechanical papers, X-Ray development, etc., they are not usually suitable for the development of ordinary general photographic materials.

Ilford Contrast and X-Ray Formula

Dissolve chemicals in this order	High Contrast	Med. Contrast
Sodium sulphite, anhydrous	150·0gm (1oz)	72·0gm (315·5gr)
Potassium carbonate, anhydrous	100·0gm (1oz)	—
Sodium carbonate, anhydrous	—	50·0gm (0.5oz)
Hydroquinone	50·0gm (5oz)	8·8gm (38gr)
Phenidone	1·1gm (50gr)	0·22gm (1gr)
Caustic soda	10·0gm (44gr)	—
Potassium bromide	16·0gm (70gr)	4·0gm (150·5gr)
Benzotriazole	1·1gm (5gr)	0·1gm (0·5gr)
Water to make	1litre (10oz)	1litre (10oz)
	Dilute 1:1 for use	Use undiluted

Medium High Contrast Hydroquinone Caustic Developer
A Sodium bisulphite   25·0gm   (110gr)

Hydroquinone	25·0gm	(110gr)
Potassium bromide	25·0gm	(110gr)
Water to	1000·0ml	(10oz)
B Caustic soda	45·0gm	(200gr)
Water to	1000·0ml	(10oz)

For use mix equal parts of **A** and **B** and develop for 2 minutes at 68°F. Rinse well before acid-fixing to avoid stain or use acid stop bath.

High Contrast Single Solution Hydroquinone-Caustic Developer
(Kodak D-8 Formula)

Sodium sulphite, anhydrous	90·0gm	(393gr)
Hydroquinone	45·0gm	(197gr)
Caustic soda	37·5gm	(164gr)
Potassium bromide	30·0gm	(131gr)
Water to	1000·0ml	(10oz)

For use take 2 parts stock solution to 1 part water. Develop for 2 minutes at 68°F. This developer keeps for several weeks bottled, and retains its energy for several hours in the open dish. Without loss of density, the caustic soda may be reduced to 28gm (122gr) in which case the stock solution will keep longer still.

With caustic soda in above reduced to 18gm, this formula becomes D-178, suitable for graticules, using Kodak Maximum Resolution plate. At same dilution, develop 3–4min at 68°F.

MONOBATH DEVELOPER/FIXER

FX-6a (no film speed increase)

Sodium sulphite, anhydrous	50·0gm	(0·5oz)
Hydroquinone	12·0gm	(0·25oz)
Phenidone	1·0gm	(9gr)
Sodium hydroxide	10·0gm	(88gr)
Sodium thiosulphate	90·0gm	(1·75oz)
Water to	1litre	(20oz)

The bath is adjusted to mean contrast. This can be varied to suit individual materials or conditions by altering the 'hypo' content. Between 70gm and 125gm/litre this will give a continuously graded softening of contrast; softer results than obtained at 125gm/litre are unlikely to be required. For still higher contrast, e.g., with process materials, increase hydroquinone to 15–17gm.

Making up
A little Calgon may be used. The bath may be divided into two stock solutions: (A) developing agents and sulphite; (B) hypo. On mixing add 1 pellet of sodium hydroxide per working ounce; this is quite accurate enough, and may be used when making up the bath.

Time
Slow and medium speed films will process in 4 minutes. Normal processing time 5 minutes for all films except Royal-X Pan (6 minutes). Six minutes is the safe time for the bath at all stages. Agitate continuously for ½ minute on pouring in, then at each minute about 15–20 twists according to tank size. Wash 5–20 minutes (see general notes below).

Capacity
Nine to 12 films per litre according to density (over exposure prolongs life).

Keep in full containers until *deeply* discoloured. A cloudy deposit should form and can be filtered off if desired. If over-worked and film is not fully cleared immerse at once in an acid fixer (logically, a rapid one); such a bath may be temporarily reactivated by adding ¼–½oz of hypo, for an emergency.

UNIVERSAL DEVELOPERS

The term 'universal' is applied to a formula suitable at various dilutions for the development of a wide range of sensitised materials—plates, films, enlarging and contact printing papers, etc. Used on negative materials, such formulae give rapid processing, but without any refinement of grain; they are therefore unsuited to the processing of miniature 35mm films except the slowest and then in a fairly well diluted form, or for use with roll films over 33° BS, ASA 160 (settings for minimum exposure) if any real degree of enlargment is required. Their use is not recommended for Kodak Royal-X Pan, which should be developed in DK-50 or D-61a—see page 229. 'Phenidone', used in two of the following formulae, is a developing agent patented by Ilford, which replaces Metol in Metol-Hydroquinone developers with certain advantages. It is non-toxic, non-staining, confers stability during working life; and, particularly in formulae of low alkalinity, the P-Q combination is less depressed by the by-products of development, notably soluble bromide. Ilford formulae using it will also be found in the contrast and fine-grain developer sections, as well as some independent formulae employing it. The Ilford official formulae are identified by the use of the name Ilford describing the formulae.

Dissolve chemicals in this order	Ilford Universal P-Q	B.J. Universal M-Q
Metol	—	3·2gm (0·25oz)
Hydroquinone	12·0gm (52gr)	12·5gm (1oz)
Sodium sulphite, anhydrous	50·0gm (0·5oz)	56·0gm (4·5oz)
Sodium carbonate anhydrous	60·0gm (260gr)	63·0gm (5oz)
Phenidone	0·50gm (2·2gr)	—
Potassium bromide*	2·0gm (9gr)	2·0gm (70gr)
Benzotriazole†	0·2gm (1gr)	—
Water to	1000·0ml (10oz)	1000·0ml (80oz)

*For contact papers may be reduced to 1gr (0·25 gm).

†Proprietary conc. liquid Antifoggants such as Ilford I.B.T, or Johnsons 142 may be substituted, about 1cc per stock oz (35cc per stock litre) is suitable.

PRINT DEVELOPERS
FX-12

This formula is recommended when a universal formula is more often to be used for development of printing papers and positive materials of all kinds, since it is balanced to obtain stable image colour over the various grades.

Dilutions are: enlarging papers 1+3; contact papers 1+1; lantern slides 1+4; films in tanks 1+7. Development times for films will closely resemble those in recommended universal developers at the same dilutions. Warm-tone development of chloro-bromides is possible by the usual dilution (e.g., 1+6) and over-exposure techniques. The chlorquinol should be obtained as fresh as possible—buff-brown not deep brown.

For chloro-bromide development only, better control and latitude may be obtained by adding 15gm/litre (132gr per 20oz) of potassium or (less readily soluble) sodium citrate. For this purpose, '142' can be reduced by one-third.

FX-12

Sodium sulphite, anhydrous	60gm
Hydroquinone	10gm
Chlorquinol	6gm
Phenidone	0.5gm
Sodium carbonate, anhydrous	60gm
Potassium bromide	1.5gm
Johnsons 142	35cc
Water to	1000m

Kodak Special Developer D.163

D.163 is a general purpose enlarging paper developer particularly recommended for warm black tones on chloro-bromide papers such as 'Bromesko'. Use one part developer to three parts water and develop for 1½ minutes at 68°F for Bromesko glossy or 1½ to 2 minutes at 68°F for other surfaces. The latter time is suitable for most papers.

Metol	2.2gm
Sodium sulphite, anhydrous	75gm
Hydroquinone	17gm
Sodium carbonate, anhydrous	65gm
Potassium bromide	2.8gm
Water	1000cc

Soft Gradation Developer

Interest is often expressed in soft gradation print developers. It must be pointed out that if contrast is to be flattened a softer grade of paper with suitable exposure and development in a standard developer can be recommended. When a soft working developer is definitely required a commercial Azol type formula will be found useful. The following metol formula is soft working and can also be used in the two bath development of papers sometimes recommended in conjunction with a standard M-Q or P-Q formula.

Ansco 120

Water 125°F	750cc
Metol	12.5gm
Sodium sulphite	36gm
Sodium carbonate, anhydrous	30gm
Potassium bromide	1.8gm
Water to	1litre

May be used full strength or at dilutions up to 1+4, according to contrast required. Average dilution 1+2. Also suitable for negative development.

STOP BATHS

(1) Stop Bath

Acetic acid glacial	20cc
or	
Acetic acid 28%	75cc
Water to	1litre

This stop bath is recommended for negative development and will remove any surface scum formed. It loses its acid vinegar smell after use.

(2) Stop Bath

Sodium bisulphite	25gm
Water, to make	1litre

An efficient and inexpensive bath, an acid smell denotes its acidity is maintained.

(3) Stop Bath Hardener

Chrome alum	20gm
Water to	1litre

This stop bath has a hardening action and deteriorates in colour from its original purple to green blue as its action is lost. It is used for negative emulsions normally, although it can be used as a final hardener for prints.

FIXERS

(1) Acid Fixing Bath

'Hypo' (sodium thiosulphate)	250gm
Sodium bisulphite	20gm
Water to	1litre

This acid fixer is of standard composition and will work as a general purpose bath for all fixing purposes. If the acid smell is lost it can be topped up again with a little bisulphite until it is regained.

(2) Acid Fixing Bath (Buffered)

'Hypo' (sodium thiosulphate)	250gm
Sodium sulphite, anhydrous	25gm
Acetic acid glacial	25cc

or

Acetic acid 28%	80cc
Water to	1litre

This is a 'buffered' fixing bath which has improved efficiency during use as a result—it has greater tolerance to carry over of developer.

(3) Buffered Acid Fixer Hardener

'Hypo' (sodium thiosulphate) crystals	300gm
Water to	1litre

Add to the above whilst stirring slowly 250cc (5oz) of the following stock hardening solution:

Sodium sulphite, anhydrous	75gm
Acetic acid glacial	65cc

or

Acetic acid 28%	235cc
Boric acid (crystals)	50gm
Potassium alum	75gm
Water to	1litre

Dissolve these constituents in the order given in half the total quantity of water at about 125°F to dissolve the boric acid quickly—or this can be done separately. Make up with cold water to the total volume.

This formula is probably the finest acid fixer hardener available—it is fully buffered for a long and efficient working life. It is particularly suitable for the processing of small format films where the operator wishes to use the most careful technique. It is also perfectly suited to the fixing of papers but a simpler formula such as (1) or (2) will fulfil requirements.